# THE **WEAVERS'** SONG BOOK

# THE WEAVERS' SONG BOOK

## Edited by The Weavers

Editorial Supervision by Ronnie Gilbert

## Arranged for piano and guitar

## by Robert De Cormier

HARPER & ROW, PUBLISHERS · NEW YORK, EVANSTON, AND LONDON

THE WEAVERS' SONG BOOK

# Ten Years with The Weavers

## A PERSONAL REPORT

### by *The Weavers*

In the Greenwich Village of Colonial days there was a stream called Minetta Brook, along whose winding course lads and lasses used to stroll, perhaps to pause and sing courting songs. We don't know this for a fact, but the population has grown since then, so it's reasonable to assume that they did.

The Weavers began their first rehearsing on that same spot, technically speaking. The brook was not the same pleasant stream it was. The aggradation of progress during the years had forced the aimless little creek underground, to find its own way through the pilings and basements of the Village.

We met in a damp basement on Macdougal Street above the brook which still ate away at the flooring in a constant effort to climb back into the sun, where little streams belong. More than once we would thoughtlessly tilt our chairs back, only to have the hind legs go through the floor. It seems to be as difficult to subdue a good brook as it is to forget the songs which were once heard along its banks.

The great thing about Greenwich Village and New York City generally is that you can always find other people interested in the same things you are, from aardvarks to zymurgy. We have not had much occasion to discuss the aardvark situation with anyone; but we and our friends have managed to keep the zymurgists working overtime. As to folk music, that is probably easier to find than anything else, in a big city made up of folks from every singing country in the world.

People have often taken The Weavers to be a family group and more than once we have been greeted with a "Hello, Miss Weaver," or "Howdy, Mr. Weaver." This is to be expected; there have been a number of singing families, such as the Hutchinson Family Singers of the Civil War Period, and the Carter Family of our times.

But none of us is named Weaver and no two of us are related. Most of the weaving we do is the toe-trodding moving in and out we do on stage. But we are a musical family, bound together by a love of the folk music of our own country and of all countries, and by our sure knowledge that as a group we can do more to bring "our" songs to people than we can do as individuals.

For the worth of a creative group is far more than the sum of its parts. In addition to the added perspective and taste which each of us derives from the years of experience of the others, there is also the fact that our repertory is more than quadrupled. Our repertory becomes larger than the total number of songs we know because the old songs keep giving birth to new ones.

We often talk about "our" songs. Sometimes we look at a song and conclude that it is not a Weavers' song. Some years back, the producer of the motion picture *High Noon* brought the theme song to our dressing room; he thought we were the right artists to make the first official recording. He was considerably dismayed when we handed the music back to him with the comment that it was not a Weavers' song. A year later, when the song *High Noon* was the hottest disc in the parade, the producer asked us whether we were sorry we had turned it down. We had said no, that it probably was the right song for its purpose, but that if we had sung it we would not have sounded quite honest.

We don't mean to say that all of us are in quick agreement about every song we consider. Far from it. Our labors sometimes generate heat. A lot of refining and hammering goes on before a song shapes up to general satisfaction.

The Weavers were singing for fun, in those days of '49, and it was not our conscious plan to aim for a professional career. We have often thought we were created by a vacuum, that is, by the lack of other song groups. There were dozens of guitar pickers and banjo players and solo singers, and an occasional chorus and folk dance group but no effective quartet in the field.

We began to sing in small gatherings, at People's Songs Hootenannies, at places like the Brooklyn Museum and on the municipal radio station, WNYC, and we were surprised at the immediate response we got. In a short time we got so many invitations that we were forced to consider the problem of a name. We could not proceed as "the nameless quartet" as Oscar Brand used to introduce us.

But finding a name takes time. Pete Seeger and Lee Hays had some experience with this problem when, in 1940, they formed a singing group with Woody Guthrie and Millard Lampell and went around the country singing folk and labor songs. This group was the Almanac Singers.

So we christened ourselves The Weavers, and our name meant that we were weavers of songs, if you pleased, or that we were inspired by the six weavers of Dorset, or by Hauptmann's weavers, or whatever. We did not want a name that pinned us down to any one kind of song, like cowboy or hillbilly songs. We wanted to sing music of such wide range that no specific name could describe it all.

In time, our name acquired a meaning and our audiences began to expect of us just what we tried to give them, songs adapted to our own manner and ability. Such a repertory could become an aimless jumble, but we did find a theme to hold ourselves and our repertory together. When we search for a title for a concert we still come back to the same one we started with: *A Musical Trip Around the World.*

We don't want to mislead anyone into thinking that we claim to be musical experts in the culture of many countries. There are many singers whose range of language is far greater than ours. Most of our songs are from our own country. What we try to do with our theme is to express great respect for the culture of all people, placing none above the others, and we sing as many songs of other peoples as we have the ability to sing. Without International Phonetics, to be honest, we could not sing nearly as many languages as we do, for we are not language students.

Fred Hellerman and Pete Seeger might be called world travelers, if not always by their own choice.

During the war Fred Hellerman was a guest of the U.S. Coast Guard on cruises that took him from Brazil to Ascension Island and the Azores to Greenland and Iceland and back to Brooklyn College. He first began to play guitar on shipboard. In college he found a number of students who were enjoying their first taste of folk music, and with them Fred began to sing and play at campus affairs, and at wingdings and hoots. He also did some acting. His professional life began with The Weavers, with whom he developed a fine talent for writing words and music. During the past few years Fred has had a busy career as a songwriter (using the pseudonym of Fred Brooks), as an arranger and accompanist. He has arranged for Harry Belafonte, Theo Bikel, The Kingston Trio and many other singers and groups. He has been a guitar accompanist, conductor, arranger, and producer for well over fifty LPs in the past few years. Many of his songs have been recorded by Harry Belafonte and other artists.

Pete Seeger worked on Saipan during the war, with a little country jazz band, entertaining soldiers in the island bases. Hearing and learning the music of the people themselves led Pete to a conclusion he has been demonstrating ever since, that there are many similarities in the music of diverse cultures, often more than there are differences. Pete began his work in folk music as an assistant to Alan Lomax in the Archive of Folk Music in the Library of Congress. He began to travel around the country, sometimes with Woody Guthrie, with the Almanacs, or alone, singing his way in union halls and in mountains and valleys where he swapped songs with banjo players. He has been making a series of films to record techniques for playing folk instruments. He went to Trinidad to film the making of the steel drum, a newly invented instrument.

As an indication of the growth of interest in folk music, Pete has found that his college concerts attract as many as two thousand, on campuses where, only a few years ago, only a hundred or two would attend. In January of 1958, with great reluctance, Pete resigned from The Weavers to devote full time to his personal concert career and to the many projects that have demanded his time and prevented him from working on even a limited schedule with The Weavers.

At sixteen Ronnie Gilbert left home in New York to live and work in wartime Washington, D.C. There a friend introduced her to a group of singers known as the "Priority Ramblers," who sang folk songs and war-effort ditties. "I was voted in by a very thin majority," Ronnie says. "They seemed to feel that my repertory of torch songs, Bach chorales and Gilbert and Sullivan roles wouldn't be of much use to them." Actually, despite ten years of musical study and performance, Ronnie was only then getting acquainted with American folk music, hearing for the first time recordings of great early jazz singers and musicians, listening awestruck to Negro congregational singing and getting her first taste of American country music.

A few years and many hootenannies later, when The Weavers were formed, Ronnie brought to the group an abiding rapport and enthusiasm for all forms of folk music, including those of other countries. She was still a little timid about singing with performers about whom she heard so much, and it took a while to cure that—about three performances. To balance vocally with three bellowing males she simply had to belt it out, and she really did.

We've always been impressed by Ronnie's bearing on stage. She's not mannered and disdains the empty gestures that many singers are trained to use. To her the only important thing is to "get inside the song." Her songs have always been high points in our programs.

In the past few years Ronnie has been engaged in many non-Weaver enterprises, including an album for R.C.A. Victor, "The Legend of Bessie Smith." Vanguard Records is at this writing preparing LPs featuring Ronnie as a solo artist. In addition to performing and songwriting she is much involved with helping other performers over the hurdles of programming, repertory, and recording.

When Pete Seeger resigned, our problem was not to "replace Pete," but to seek a fourth Weaver who we felt could on his own make a contribution to our group both from an instrumental and voice point of view. We were unanimous in our selection of Erik Darling. Erik worked with the Tarriers, another folk-song group which has been heard on the hit parade. Erik came from upper New York State to New York City, where he studied banjo and guitar and hoped to learn songs from the many young people who come to the big city from everywhere. Erik has been with The Weavers long enough to write some new songs with us. On his own he has issued his own album, and has taken part in recording sessions with many other performers. Erik has recorded as an accompanist for many artists and has also made an LP of his own issued by Elektra records.

Lee Hays' musical life began in Arkansas in the twenties, when he sang in country churches and at fish fries. He has often said that he did not know he was singing folk songs until he came to New York in the thirties and was informed of the fact by educated friends. As a child he used to visit Negro churches and sit in the back pew, and he used to visit the homes of Negro farmers, soaking up the richest musical sounds and harmonies that have ever come our way.

The Weavers sometimes kid him with the remark that no matter what he sings, Hebrew, Spanish, or Indonesian, it all comes out sounding like a Methodist hymn. Once you get foursquare harmony in your system, it is there to stay.

Lee has never regarded himself as a performer, in the sense that each of the others is a performer. Like the submerged nine-tenths of an iceberg, his chief interest is in the writing, preparation, and imagining that goes on before a song is ready to be made visible. Lee has been a writer of many mystery stories, some of which have appeared as prize selections in the top mystery magazines. He is a columnist for the *Brooklyn Heights Press,* his community paper, and is also one of the members of the "Baby Sitters Quartet" that have put out two LPs of folk material for children, issued by Vanguard Records.

We must mention other persons who have contributed to our work. We began our career with the help of Toshi Seeger, Pete's wife, who negotiated our first night-club contract (she got us each fifty dollars a week and free sandwiches). We stayed in that club for six months and the pay went up as we went along, though we had to struggle to maintain our sandwich rights. It was there we met Gordon Jenkins, the popular composer, who fell in love with our songs and who steered us into our first recording contract. We remember the cynical advice of a recording company executive who said, "You've got to decide whether you want to be good or commercial." Our feeling and Gordon's was that we should try to be good *and* commercial, for we saw no barrier between the two.

As our recordings began to take hold we found we needed a manager. We were lucky: we found two. They were Harold Leventhal and Pete Kameron, who had worked in the music business for some time. Their guidance kept us working on the right roads; for example, they would not let us appear in certain places until we had had more experience and were ready. If we had followed our own judgment we might have been detoured at the outset.

For admittedly we were greenhorns. When we were working in the Village Vanguard in New York, a man said to us, after a show, "You have a fine act." We said, with some astonishment, "It's not an act, it's real!" We thought of acts as dancing dogs, or acrobats; it never occurred to us that even a single singer is an act, in the trade.

We have worked most closely with Harold Leventhal, who is our personal manager and close friend, and the fifth Weaver. He has held us together during trying times. It is his creative role to bring us and our audiences together. When he reunited us for our Carnegie Hall concert in 1955, after a period of unemployment, we took as much pleasure from Harold's deep satisfaction over the success of the occasion as we did from our own work.

We could not begin to name all the persons who have helped us. It was our privilege to sing with Huddie Ledbetter, who was called Leadbelly, and we feel his presence whenever we sing, for his songs are always with us. Woody Guthrie is a significant name in folk music and his in-fluence has been strong.

We are great admirers of Mahalia Jackson, and one of the honors we have enjoyed was singing with her and Richard Dyer-Bennett on a television show. We worked with the late Big Bill Broonzy, and with Sonny Terry, who plays beautiful harmonica music, and we have worked with almost every folk singer we could name.

The initial preparation of this book was interrupted when we left for a summer's work in Israel and the British Isles. It was a musical trip halfway around the world, and we visited the home grounds of many of the songs we sing. We found that our songs had already begun to be known in Israel, as their exciting music is becoming known here, and that American folk songs have a greater audience in Europe than ever before. Folk singers like Cisco Houston, Sonny Terry and Brownie McGee are touring India and the Orient. The time is surely at hand when the word "strange" will be obsolete as applied to the folk culture of any of the peoples of the world.

As we have indicated before, we do not feel that our songs are truly ours until they have become yours. A song on paper means very little until you have given it life through your own voice and shaped it to your own feeling and style of singing. Fortunately you are not obliged to like every song in the book; but we hope you will find many that you do like well enough to make them your own.

As we end our first ten years of work, we feel that we are just beginning. Decades to come cannot be more exciting and rewarding then the first one. It is a privilege and honor to weave songs for you.

THE WEAVERS

We cannot adequately express our thanks to the staff of Harper's, especially Dee Delano, Hal Grove, Dolores Simon and Bob Bullen, who, unaware of the mysterious ways of folk singers, nevertheless managed with incredible patience and good humor to urge, cajole and press us onward to the completion of this book. Their devotion to the tradition of fine publishing made possible some of the best aspects of this book, such as the beautiful autography, which is the work of Max Weaner. To Bob Silverman go our especial thanks for the many helpful suggestions arising out of hours of thoughtful and painstaking proofreading. We are also indebted to Howie Richman and Al Brackman for their cooperation in the use of song material.

# Introductory Note

To most readers of a book like this the crediting of material is of minor interest. To say therefore that the name "Paul Campbell," to which many of the songs in this book are assigned, was a pseudonym adopted from 1950 to 1953 for Ronnie Gilbert, Lee Hays, Fred Hellerman and Peter Seeger should ordinarily suffice. However, The Weavers' employment of a nom de plume had a significance considerably beyond its use as a publishing device.

In 1950, when The Weavers made their professional debut, they came into the commercial music world not so much as performers but rather as a sort of performing workshop, in which each member functioned at times and to varying degrees as lyricist, composer, editor, arranger, and researcher as well as singer and actor. In doing so we were hardly being original. Throughout history, musicians, poets, storytellers, tutored and untrained, have been doing just that and have been giving the world the never-ending flow of literature and music that in this country we call "folk song." Indeed it is by being subjected over a period of time to this handling and rehandling by many people that a song or combination of songs takes on that patina that identifies it as a folk song.

The contribution to a given song of a housewife, a café singer, lumberman and penitentiary prisoner cannot possibly be estimated by even the great professional collectors like Sharp, Botkin and the Lomaxes. Yet the intentional or accidental creative work of such unrecorded "sources" is implicit in every recorded and published variant.

It is with this kind of music that The Weavers were and are concerned, a music highly fluid in nature in which editing, adding, changing, often almost total rewriting are appropriate and necessary. The result of weeks, sometimes months, of work on such material is a body of songs that in the music industry of that time came to be known as "Weavers' songs," as indeed they were, for inevitably they took on the characteristics of the group and the individuals in it. In just this way does a "blues song" or a so-called "Calypso," though it may be the blending of endless borrowings from dozens of singers, come to be at last identified with a Leadbelly, a Blind Blake, or a Big Bill Broonzy who loves it, takes it and remakes it for his own.

In the highly complex realm of recording and publishing of 1950, The Weavers found little precedent for processing material produced through our accustomed *modus operandi*. In this book are pieces which are enlargements of fragments of otherwise forgotten songs. There are songs which are the result of combining elements of several songs. Sometimes our contribution is no more than a unique arrangement, an added verse or a line or two, or the simple restatement of the story or melody as we originally heard it. There are others which are totally the creation of one or another member of the group, edited and reworked by the others. To those songs which were published during the period between 1950 and 1953 we assigned the name "Paul Campbell," as representing both the combined efforts of the four people then known as The Weavers and the concept of musical work to which they were committed.

# Contents

## ABOUT THE CONTENTS

The Weavers were never able to resist becoming intrigued with many areas of folk material. Consequently the songs in this book cover a variety of subject matter such as defies technical categorization. Yet, for many songbook users, a classified index is often helpful, and to try to meet that need we devised the table of contents that follows. We hope that it will also help illustrate our own approach to folk material.

The headings represent the universal components of ordinary daily life, from which all folk songs derive, that "simple" life which is made up of the immense complexity of human experience. The songs in each category are a free but tiny sampling of the endlessly individualistic comments of the "common man" on the given subject. He gripes about, damns, satirizes, mourns or, occasionally, praises his work and the conditions of his life. He sings of love, false and true, its causes, effects, controls and cures—weeps at it, laughs at it and lies about it and is only rarely sure if he's pro it or con it. And as love is often a tiring diversion he often needs lighter amusement and provides himself and his kids with banjo tunes, dance and game songs and the biggest whoppers he can tell with a straight face. And when his conscience is awakened by the challenge of larger dreams and strong convictions he sings, as he cannot always speak, of the stirrings of his soul.

(For the convenience of those readers who might like to use the printed songs in conjunction with recordings the material has been so grouped in the book as to follow approximately the contents of the Vanguard records on which most of the songs have appeared. These are: The Weavers at Carnegie Hall, Vol. I; The Weavers on Tour; The Weavers at Home; and Travelling on with the Weavers.)

# OF FUN AND PLAY

# OF IDEAS AND IDEALS

### HYMNS AND SPIRITUALS

### ESPECIALLY FOR THE CHRISTMAS-CHANUKAH SEASON

# About the Guitar Chords

Each diagram represents the top end of the guitar fingerboard as though one were looking down on the flat surface of the fingerboard. Each vertical line represents a guitar string; each horizontal line, a fret.

A black dot (.) on the diagram designates the point at which a string should be pressed to produce a chord.

A small circle (o) over an unfingered string indicates that the string should be played with the chord, even though it is not fingered.

If neither (o) nor (.) is indicated for any string, such string should *not* be played with the chord. In certain instances, a small cross (x) has been used to emphasize the point that a string marked in this manner should not be played.

A small arc ($\cap$) across several strings indicates a "bar" chord. Such chords should be played with the first finger of the left hand across all the strings included in the arc.

## About Chords *Not* Appearing in the Diagrams

The actual number of possible chord formations is infinite. Ninths, sixths, major sevenths, etc., are additions to basic chords which, like whipped cream or icing on a cake, can be pleasant touches but rarely change the basic character or essence of the chord (or cake, as the case may be). Since it would be impossible to include every possible chord, those chords for which no diagrams appear may be dealt with in the following manner:

Ninths — May be played as *sevenths*. (For example: where $D^9$ appears, substitute $D^7$; for $Em^9$, play $Em^7$, etc.)

†Major sevenths
Sixths — May be omitted, in which case the chord should be played in its basic form. (For example: G may be played instead of $G^6$; E instead of $E^6$; C instead of $C maj^7$; etc.)

†Major seventh chords are quite commonly confused with seventh chords. They are *not* one and the same. $C^7$ is quite different from $Cmaj^7$.

## Important

Chord diagrams marked with an asterisk (*) indicate movable chords. Accordingly, even though a diagram for $C\sharp m^7$ does not appear, the chord marked $Cm^7$, if moved one fret higher, would produce a $C\sharp m^7$. Similarly, to find $G\sharp$, move the $F\sharp$ chord two frets higher, and so on. In this manner, any chord for which no diagram appears may be found.

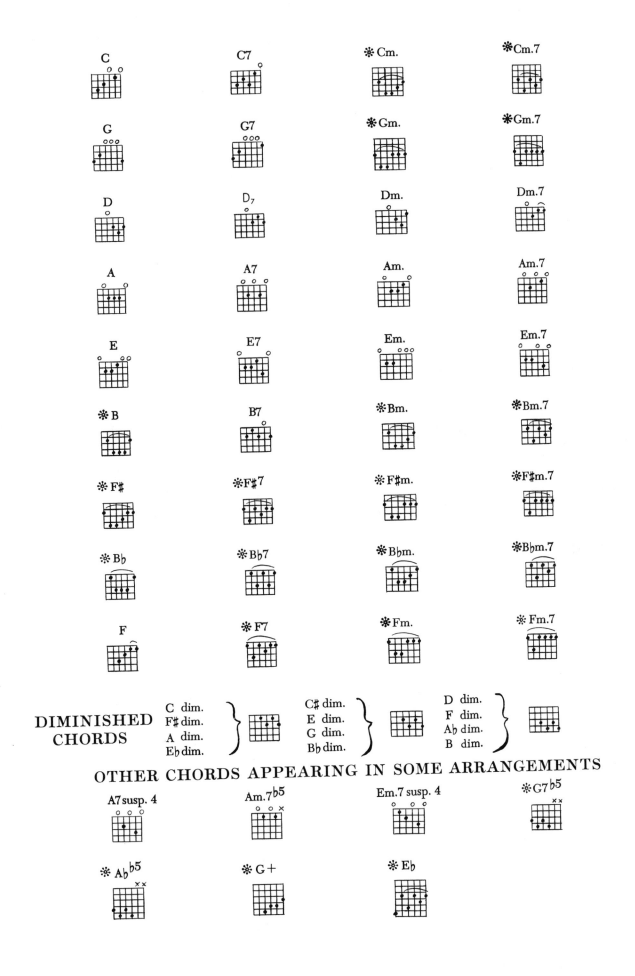

DIMINISHED CHORDS

OTHER CHORDS APPEARING IN SOME ARRANGEMENTS

# When the Saints Go Marching In

A foot-stomping old gospel hymn which sounds best
when a harmonizing crowd brings in the responses
after each phrase of the melody.

Additional words and music by The Weavers (Paul Campbell)

shore._____ 1. Oh, when the saints _____ go march - ing in, _____
vealed. _____ 2.(And when the) sun _____ be - gins to shine, _____
3.(Oh, when the) trum - - pet sounds a call, _____

\_\_\_ Oh, when the saints go march - ing in, _____
\_\_\_ And when the sun be - gins to shine, _____ Oh, Lord, I
\_\_\_ Oh, when the trum - pet sounds a call, _____

want to be in that num - ber, _____ When the

saints go march - ing in. _____ 2. And when the
sun be - gins to shine. _____ 3. Oh, when the
trum - pet sounds a

call. _____     4. Some___  vealed._____

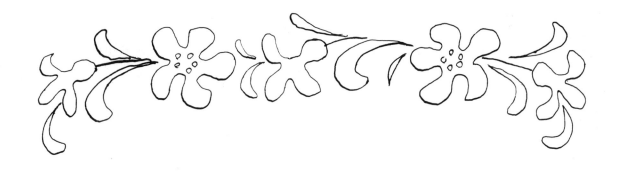

# Kisses Sweeter Than Wine

Leadbelly reminded us of the tune, which
was once an Irish lament for a dead cow,
and we made up the new words. Of all our
original songs, this one seems to be one of
the most enduring.

Words by Paul Campbell (The Weavers), music by Joel Newman (Huddie Ledbetter)

Oh, _____ kiss-es sweet-er than wine, _____

Oh, _____ kiss-es sweet-er than

wine. _____ 1. When I was a young man and nev-er been kissed_ I got to
2. He asked me to mar-ry and be his sweet wife,_ And we would

think-ing  ov-er  what I  had missed.__  I  got me  a  girl,  I
be  so  hap-py  all  of  our  life, ___  He begged and  he plead-ed  like a

kissed  her  and then __  Oh  Lord,  I  kissed her  a-gain.
nat-u-ral man,__  and then  Oh  Lord,  I  gave him my hand.

*D. C. al FINE*

3. I worked mighty hard and so did my wife,
   Workin' hand in hand to make a good life.
   Corn in the field and wheat in the bins, I was,
   Oh Lord, the father of twins. *(Chorus)*

4. Our children numbered just about four,
   And they all had sweethearts knockin' at the door.
   They all got married and didn't hesitate; I was,
   Oh Lord, the grandmother of eight. *(Chorus)*

5. Now we are old, and ready to go,
   We get to thinkin' what happened a long time ago.
   Had a lot of kids, trouble and pain, but,
   Oh Lord, we'd do it again. *(Chorus)*

# Suliram

The melody of this lullaby is strongly European—probably Dutch—but the Indonesian words follow the style of typical indigenous songs. The words go: "Hush, baby. Now that I've found you I won't let you go. Early in the morning as the sun was rising, I saw a water buffalo slain."

Based on traditional Indonesian song

Ba - ru - se kla - rung sai - ya —— men - da - bat. La su - li

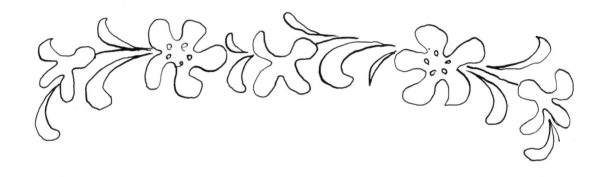

# Hard, Ain't It Hard

To love one who never did love you is not just hard;
it's hard *and* it's hard, and man, that's *hard*.

Additional words and music by Woody Guthrie (based on traditional song)

(Chorus)

Well, it's ___ hard, and it's hard, ain't it hard ___
___ To love one who nev-er did love you? ___
___ And it's hard, and it's hard, ain't it hard, Good Lord, To
love one who nev-er ___ will be true? ___

*Verse*

1. There is a house in this old town, ___ That's where my
2. First time that I saw my true love ___ He was a-

true love hangs a-round. ___ He takes all the wom-en right down on his
walk-in' by my door, ___ The next time I saw his false-heart-ed

knee And he tells them ___ a lit-tle tale he won't tell me. ___
smile He was lay-in' dead and cold up-on the floor. ___

3. Who's gonna kiss your ruby lips?
   Who's gonna hold you to his breast?
   And who's gonna talk your future over
   While I'm out a-ramblin' in the West? (*Chorus*)

4. Don't go to drinkin' or to gamblin',
   Don't go there your sorrow to drown.
   That hard-liquor place is a low-down disgrace,
   It's the meanest old place in the town. (*Chorus*)

# Follow the Drinking Gourd

A map and timetable for the Underground Railway:
Follow the Big Dipper; it points to the North—and
freedom.

Based on traditional song,
new adaptation by Lee Hays

car - ry you to free - dom, Fol - low the drink - in' gourd. 1. When the
2. Now the

*FINE*

*Verse*

sun comes back and the first quail calls,— Fol - low the drink - in' gourd.— The
riv - er bank -'ll make a might-y good road,— The dead trees will show you the way. —

old man is a - wait-in' For to car - ry you to free-dom, Fol- low the drink- in' gourd.
Left foot, peg foot, trav- el - in' on, — Fol- low the drink- in' gourd.

3. Now the river ends between two hills,
   Follow the drinkin' gourd.
   There's another river on the other side,
   Follow the drinkin' gourd. *(Chorus)*

# Rock Island Line

Leadbelly used to sing this delightful verse: "Moses stood on the Red Sea shore, smotin' the water with a two-by-four." Sung as a work song, or for entertainment, the song has spawned many a new couplet. Try making some up yourself.

Additional words and music by The Weavers and Joel Newman (Huddie Ledbetter)

Oh well, the Rock Is-land Line,— It is a might-y good road,— Oh well, the Rock Is-land Line,— It is the road to ride.— The Rock Is-land Line,— It is a might-y good road,— Well, if you

3. Moses stood on the Red Sea shore,
   Smotin' the water with a two-by-four. *(Chorus)*

4. Little Evalina, sittin' in the shade,
   Countin' on the money that the Weavers ain t made. *(Chorus)*

5. Jesus died to save our sins,
   Glory to God, we're gonna need him again. *(Chorus)*

# Home in That Rock

The Bible parable speaks of Lazarus, the poor man, who begged Dives, the rich man, to give him the crumbs from his table. Dives didn't. When they died, Lazarus went to heaven and Dives went to hell, where he begged Lazarus to bring him a few drops of water. Lazarus didn't.

Traditional

*With a solid gospel beat*

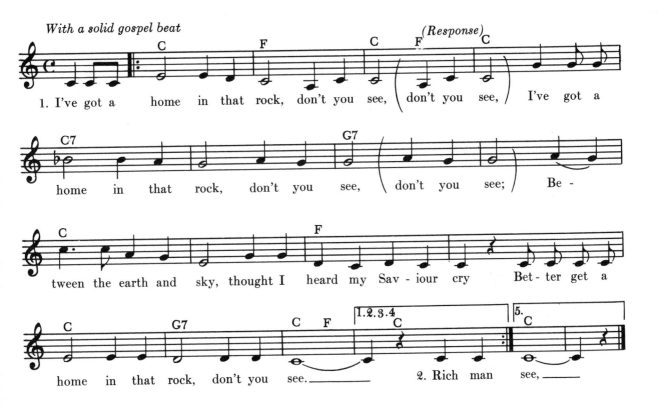

1. I've got a home in that rock, don't you see, don't you see, I've got a home in that rock, don't you see, don't you see; Be- tween the earth and sky, thought I heard my Sav - iour cry Bet - ter get a home in that rock, don't you see._____ 2. Rich man see,_____

2. Rich man Dives, he lived so well, don't you see, don't you see, *(twice)*
   Rich man Dives lived so well, when he died he had a home in hell,
   He had no home in that rock, don't you see.

3. Poor man Lazarus, poor as I, don't you see, don't you see, *(twice)*
   Poor man Lazarus, poor as I, when he died he had a home on high,
   He had a home in that rock, don't you see.

4. God gave Noah the rainbow sign, don't you see, don't you see, *(twice)*
   God gave Noah the rainbow sign, no more water but fire next time,
   You better get a home in that rock, don't you see.

5. Better get a home in that rock, don't you see, don't you see, *(twice)*
   Between the earth and sky, thought I heard my Saviour cry
   Better get a home in that rock, don't you see.

# I Know Where I'm Going

A Scottish ballad of a girl who knew exactly what she wanted.

Traditional

*Simply but with feeling*

1. I know where I'm go- ing And I know who's go- ing
2. Feath- er beds are soft And paint- ed rooms are

with me; I know who I love And my dear knows who I'll
bon- nie, But I would trade them all For my hand- some, win- some

mar- ry. Well, I have stock-ings of silk And shoes of bright green
John- ny. Now, some say he's bad, But I say he's

leath - er, / bon - nie,

Combs to buck- le my hair, ___ / Fair - est of ___ them all ___

And a / Is my

ring for ev - 'ry fin - ger. / hand - some, win - some

Johnny.

2nd time rit.

# Venga Jaleo

It is said that during the Spanish Civil War the poet
García Lorca wrote the words to this theme, which
occurs in more than one old Spanish song.

Traditional, as sung by Spanish Republican Army

*With intensity and fervor*

1. El

*Verse*

diez   y   o -   cho de   jul- io, _____   En el   pa -   tio
ter   y   Cam -   pe - si -   no,   Con Ga- lan   y

de un con - ven -  to_____   El _____   pue -   blo _____   ma - dri - 
con _____   Mo - des -   to, _____   Con el   co -   man -   dan - te

18

le- ño \_\_\_\_\_ Fun- dó el Quin -to Re - gi - mien - to.\_\_\_\_\_
Car- los \_\_\_\_\_ No hay mi- li - cia - no con mie - do.\_\_\_\_\_

(Chorus)

Ven - ga ja - le - o, ja - le - o!\_\_\_\_\_ Sue - ño de u - na a-

me - tra - lla - do - ra, Y Fran - co se va pa - se - o, y

Fran - co se va pa - se - o.\_\_\_\_\_

2. Con Lis -

19

3. Con el Quinto, Quinto, Quinto,
   Con el Quinto Regimiento,
   Madre, yo me voy al frente
   Para las lineas de fuego!


*Translation*   1. On the eighteenth of July,
                   In the courtyard of a convent,
                   The people of Madrid
                   Formed the Fifth Regiment.

                2. With Lister and Campesino,
                   With Galan and with Modesto,
                   With Carlos, the commander,
                   There's no soldier who's afraid.

                3. With the Fifth, Fifth, Fifth,
                   With the Fifth Regiment,
                   Mother, I am going to the front
                   For the firing lines.

        *Chorus*    Come, clap out the rhythm—
                    Dream of a machine gun
                    And Franco will do the walking!

# Darling Corey

A wild Kentucky song about a wild lady moonshiner.
The rule for singing this song is: Let yourself go; let
joy be unrefined.

Adaptation and arrangement by The Weavers (Paul Campbell)

1. Wake up, wake up, _____
hole, dig a hole _____

Dar-lin' Cor-ey, _____
in the mead-ow, _____
What makes you sleep _ so
Dig a hole in the cold,_ cold

sound? The _ rev-e-nue of-fi-cers are com-in', _____
ground, Dig a hole, dig a hole in the mead-ow, _____

Gon-na tear your still - house down.     2. Well, the
Gon-na lay Dar- lin' Cor - ey

first time I seen _____    Dar-lin' Cor-ey, \_\_    She was stand-in' by \_\_ the
'way, go 'way, _____    Dar-lin' Cor-ey, \_\_    Quit hang- in' 'round \_ my
yes, oh yes, _____    my dar-lin', \_\_    I'll do the best \_ I

sea,    Had a for - ty - five strapped a -round her bo - som, \_\_
bed,    Bad \_ lik - ker has ruined my bo - dy, \_\_
can,    But I'll nev - er give my pleas - ure \_\_

Had a ban - jo   on ___ her   knee.   3. Go
Pret-ty wo - men   gone to   my   head.   4. Oh,
To an-oth - er   gam -   blin'   man.   5. Dig a

Coda

down. ___

# Hush, Little Baby

"Aunt Rhody" is number one on the all-time lullaby
hit parade; and this is probably number two.

Traditional

3. And if that billy goat don't pull,
    Papa's gonna buy you a cart and bull,
    And if that cart and bull turn over,
    Papa's gonna buy you a dog named Rover.

4. And if that dog named Rover don't bark,
    Papa's gonna buy you a horse and cart,
    And if that horse and cart fall down,
    You'll still be the sweetest little baby in town.

# Pay Me My Money Down

A song of the Georgia Sea Islands.

By Lydia A. Parrish

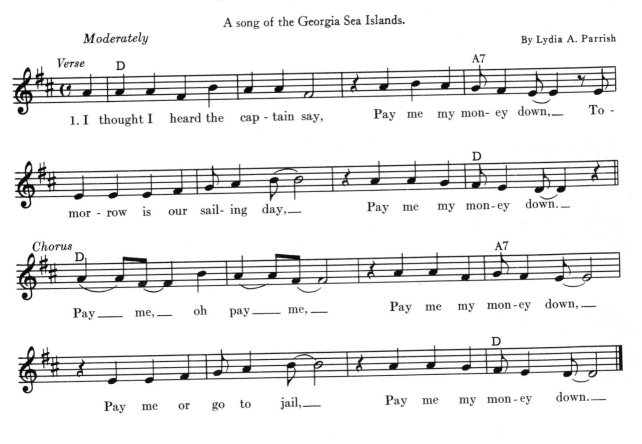

2. As soon as the boat was clear of the bar,
    Pay me my money down,
    He knocked me down with the end of a spar,
    Pay me my money down. *(Chorus)*

3. I wish I was Mr. Howard's son,
    Pay me my money down,
    Sit in the house and drink good rum,
    Pay me my money down. *(Chorus)*

4. Well, I wish I was Mr. Steven's son,
    Pay me my money down,
    Sit on the bank and watch the work done,
    Pay me my money down. *(Chorus)*

# Lonesome Traveller

A modern spiritual, with driving rhythm and subtle off-beats. We suggest that you ad-lib your own rises and falls to build the song toward the direction of your own excitement.

Words and music by Lee Hays

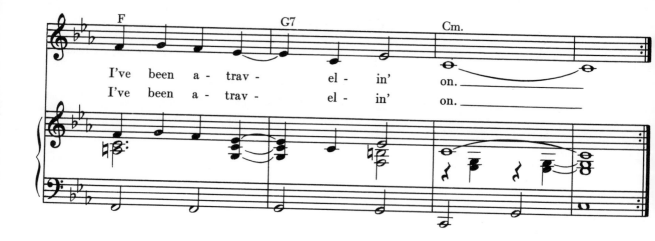

I've been a - trav - el - in' on. ____
I've been a - trav - el - in' on. ____

5. Traveled with the rich, traveled with the poor,
   Well, I traveled with the rich, traveled with the poor,
   Traveled with the rich, traveled with the poor,
   I've been a-travelin' on.

6. One of these days, I'm gonna stop all my travelin',
   One of these days, I'm gonna stop all my travelin',
   One of these days, I'm gonna stop all my travelin',
   I've been a-travelin' on.

7. Gonna keep right on a-trav'lin' on the road to freedom,
   Gonna keep right on a-trav'lin' on the road to freedom,
   Gonna keep right on a-trav'lin' on the road to freedom,
   Gonna keep right on a-trav'lin' on.

# Wimoweh

An instrumental song for voices. It came to us from South Africa, as sung by singers in city cafés. The original Zulu words mean "The lion is sleeping."

Based on a traditional South African song

Oo, _____

oo, _____ oo, _____

*Open tone*

Ah,— ah, — ah,—

ah,— ah,— la la la la, _____ Ah,—

ah, —     ah, —     ah, —     ah, —

Ah, —     ah, —     wi - mo - weh. —

# Goodnight Irene

For years this was the theme song of Huddie Ledbetter, better known as Leadbelly, King of the Twelve-String Guitar. The Weavers sang with him many times and learned many songs from him, such as this ballad of the girl who married a rounder and a bounder.

Words and music by Huddie Ledbetter and John Lomax

I - rene, good night; _____ I - rene, good night; _____ Good night, I - rene, good night, I - rene, I'll see you in my dreams. _____

**Verse**

1. Last Sat-ur-day night I got mar-ried, _____ Me and my
2. Some-times I live in the coun-try, _____ Some-times I

wife set-tled down, _____ Now me and my wife _____ are
live in town, _____ Some-times I take a great

part-ed, _____ I'm gon-na take an-oth-er stroll down-town. _____
no-tion _____ To jump in-to the riv-er and drown. _____

*D. C. al FINE*

3. She caused me to weep, she caused me to mourn,
   Caused me to leave my home,
   But the very last words I heard her say
   Was, "Please sing me one more song." *(Chorus)*

4. Stop ramblin', stop your gamblin',
   Stop stayin' out late at night;
   Go home to your wife and your family;
   Stay there by your fireside bright. *(Chorus)*

# On Top of Old Smoky

The Smokies, so called because of the fog in the valleys, are the home site of many and many an American folk song.

*Words in italics to be spoken.

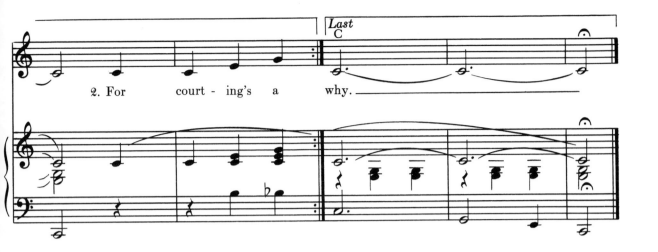

2. For court - ing's a why. _____

3. A thief will just rob you *(And take what you have)
   And take what you have, (But a false-hearted lover)
   But a false-hearted lover (Will lead you to the grave)
   Will lead you to the grave. (And the grave will decay you)

4. And the grave will decay you (And turn you to dust)
   And turn you to dust, (Not one boy in a hundred)
   Not one boy in a hundred (A poor girl can trust)
   A poor girl can trust. (They'll hug you and kiss you)

5. They'll hug you and kiss you (And tell you more lies)
   And tell you more lies (Than cross-ties on a railroad)
   Than the cross-ties on a railroad (Or stars in the sky)
   Or stars in the sky. (So, come, all you young maidens)

6. So, come all you young maidens (And listen to me)
   And listen to me, (Never place your affection)
   Never place your affection (On a green willow tree)
   On a green willow tree. (The leaves they will wither)

7. For the leaves they will wither, (The roots they will die)
   The roots they will die, (You'll all be forsaken)
   You'll all be forsaken (And never know why)
   And never know why.

*Words in italics to be spoken.

# The Frozen Logger

A tall tale of the tall tree toppers, from the North-
west logging country.

Words and music by James Stevens

*Moderately*

3. My lover was a logger,
   There's none like him today;
   If you'd pour whiskey on it
   He could eat a bale of hay.

4. He never shaved his whiskers
   From off of his horny hide;
   He'd just drive them in with a hammer
   And bite them off inside.

5. My lover came to see me
   Upon one freezing day;
   He held me in a fond embrace
   Which broke three vertebrae.

6. He kissed me when we parted,
   So hard that he broke my jaw;
   I could not speak to tell him
   He'd forgot his mackinaw.

7. I saw my lover leaving,
   Sauntering through the snow,
   Going gaily homeward
   At forty-eight below.

8. The weather it tried to freeze him,
   It tried its level best;
   At a hundred degrees below zero
   He buttoned up his vest.

9. It froze clean through to China,
   It froze to the stars above;
   At a thousand degrees below zero
   It froze my logger love.

10. And so I lost my lover,
    And to this café I come,
    And here I wait till someone
    Stirs his coffee with his thumb.

# Michael, Row the Boat Ashore

Michael's identity may be a matter for conjecture;
not so the song's. It's a real audience-catcher, inspiring big sweeping harmony at the "Hallelujahs."

Traditional song of American Negro slaves
Arranged and adapted by Tony Saletan and The Weavers

With a solid beat

Chorus

Mi- chael, row the boat a - shore, Hal - le - lu - jah, Mi - chael,

row the boat a - shore, Hal - le - lu - jah. 1. Sis - ter,
2. The riv - er is

Verse

help to trim the sails, Hal - le - lu - jah, Sis - ter,
deep and the riv - er is wide, Hal - le - lu - jah, Green - er

help      to trim the \_\_ sails,    Hal - le - lu -      jah.    Mi - chael,
pas-tures on the oth- er \_\_ side,    Hal - le - lu -      jah.

3. Jordan's river is chilly and cold, Hallelujah,
   Chills the body but not the soul, Hallelujah. *(Chorus)*

4. The river is deep and the river is wide, Hallelujah,
   Milk and honey on the other side, Hallelujah. *(Chorus)*

# We Wish You a Merry Christmas

The song begins and ends with a well-known wassail-
ing song; The Weavers have added new material to
make it a Christmas peace song.

Additional words and music by The Weavers (Paul Campbell)
Based on traditional English carol

Shan-ti! Sa - lud! Sha - lom! The words mean the same what-
ev - er your home. Why can't we have Christ - mas the whole year a-
round? __ Why can't we have Christ-mas the whole year a - round? 4. We
wish you a mer-ry Christ - mas, We wish you a mer-ry Christ -mas, We

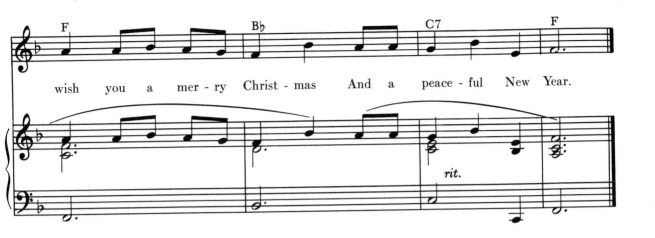

wish you a mer - ry Christ - mas And a peace - ful New Year.

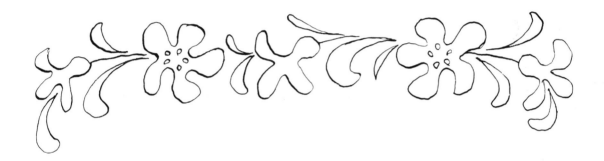

# Go Tell It on the Mountain

In singing songs like this old Christmas spiritual, The Weavers try to follow this rule: Think of Mahalia Jackson, even though you can't sing like her. It's an inspiring image.

Spiritual

Go tell it on the moun - tain That Je - sus Christ__ is born. 1. Down
2. While

in a lone - ly__ man - ger The hum - ble Christ was born, And
shep - herds kept their__ watch, ___ O'er si - lent flocks by night, Be -

*D. S. 𝄋 last time*

God sent out sal - va - tion That bless - ed Christ - mas morn.
hold! through-out the __ heav - ens There shone a ho - ly light.

# Shalom Chaverim (Glad Tidings)

"Peace, friends—till we meet again...."An ancient Hebrew greeting becomes a song for all the world to sing. The Weavers added the English words to join two great heritages.

The second time the first six words may be sung as a round, with voices entering at numbers 1, 2, 3, and 4.

English lyric and new music arrangement by The Weavers (Paul Campbell)

*Moderately*

Sha - lom cha-ver- im, sha - lom cha-ver- im, Sha - lom, sha - lom, Le - hit - ra - ot, le - hit - ra - ot, Sha - lom, sha - lom. sha - lom. Glad tid - ings we bring of peace on __ earth, Good

# Lulloo Lullay (The Coventry Carol)

This is related to the ancient song "Coventry." We've retold, in simple English, the story of the wicked king Herod.

New lyrics and music arrangement by The Weavers (Paul Campbell)

1. Lul - loo __ lul - lay, __ my tin - y child, Bye - bye, __ lul - loo __ lul -
Christ __ was born __ King He - rod was an - gry, Fear - ing the Son __ of

lay. ____ Lul - lay, __ my tin - y lit - tle child, Bye -
Man. ____ He sent __ his sol - diers forth __ to slay __ All

. bye, ____ lul - loo ____ lul - lay. ____ 2. When Day. ____
child - ren in Beth - le - hem. ____

3. All children they slew, but did not find
   Jesus, born of man.
   For He was gone, His parents fled
   With Him to Egypt Land.

4. Then they were dead who sought His life;
   The Scriptures did foretell.
   Joseph brought Mary his wife, and Jesus
   Home to Israel.

5. Lulloo lullay, my tiny child,
   Bye-bye, lulloo lullay.
   For kings all die, but babies live
   To sing on Christmas Day.

# The Seven Blessings of Mary (Traditional Carol)

There is an old carol that tells this story, which is customarily sung as a slow wail, in the Elizabethan manner. But one of The Weavers heard this rollicking version on the Cumberland Mountain of Tennessee, sung by Aunt Tutt, an old mountain singer.

*Adaptation and arrangement by The Weavers*

*Verse Reel tempo*

1. The ver-y first bless-ing that Ma-ry had,— It was the bless-ing of one, To think that her son Je-sus Was God's on-ly son, Was God's on-ly son.

*Chorus*

Come all ye to the wil-der-ness, Glo-ry, glo-ry be! Fa-ther, son, and the Ho-ly Ghost— For all e-ter-ni-ty!

2. The very next blessing that Mary had,
   It was the blessing of two,
   To think that her son Jesus
   Could read the Bible through,
   Could read the Bible through. (*Chorus*)

3. The very next blessing that Mary had,
   It was the blessing of three,
   To think that her son Jesus
   Could make the blind to see,
   Could make the blind to see. (*Chorus*)

4. The very next blessing that Mary had,
   It was the blessing of four,
   To think that her son Jesus
   Would live to help the poor,
   Would live to help the poor. (*Chorus*)

5. The very next blessing that Mary had,
   It was the blessing of five,
   To think that her son Jesus
   Could make the dead to rise,
   Could make the dead to rise. (*Chorus*)

6. Now, Mary had these blessings,
   She counted one by one.
   She knew the greatest blessing
   Was her godly son,
   Was her godly son. (*Chorus*)

7. The very last blessing that Mary had,
   It was the blessing of seven,
   To know that her son Jesus
   Was safe at last in Heav'n,
   Was safe at last in Heav'n. (*Chorus*)

# Poor Little Jesus

In the most moving spirituals there is a sense of personal concern, as if Biblical events were happening to neighbors or to the singers themselves.

*Moderately*

Additional verses by The Weavers

1. It was poor ___ lit - tle Je - sus, yes, yes, ___ He was
poor ___ lit - tle Je - sus, yes, yes, ___

born on ___ Fri - day, yes, yes, ___ Did - n't
Child ___ of ___ Ma - ry, yes, yes, ___ He was

have no ___ cra - dle, yes, yes, ___
laid ___ in a man - ger, yes, yes, ___

Was-n't that a pit-y and — a shame, oh Lord,_____

Was-n't that a pit-y and — a shame!_____ 2. It was shame!

3. It was poor little Jesus, yes, yes,
   Well, they whipped him up a mountain, yes, yes,
   And they hung him with a robber, yes, yes,
   Wasn't that a pity and a shame, oh Lord,
   Wasn't that a pity and a shame!

4. He was born on Christmas, yes, yes,
   He was born on Christmas, yes, yes,
   Didn't have no shelter, yes, yes,
   Wasn't that a pity and a shame, oh Lord,
   Wasn't that a pity and a shame!

# Mi Y'Malel

Traditional Hebrew song, celebrating the victory of Judas Maccabaeus over the Syrian invaders. The words mean: "Who can tell the things that happened to us? Who can count them? In every age a hero came to help us. At this time of year long ago, Maccabaeus restored the Temple. But now all Israel must rise united and redeem itself through work and sacrifice."

Traditional Hebrew song arranged by The Weavers

*Moderately*

Mi y' ma-lel g'vur-ot Yis-ra-el O-tan mi yim-neh?

Hen-b' chol dor ya-kum ha-gi-bor, Go-el Ha-am.

Sh' ma!_____ Ba-ya-min ha-hem baz' man ha-zeh._____

Ma-ka-bi mo-shi-a u fo-deh,_____ U v'ya men-u kol am Yis-ra-

el._____ Yi-ta-ched, ya-kum_____ yi-ga-el._____

# Burgundian Carol

In the France of 250 years ago a compassionate lawyer of Burgundy satirized the rich and the pompous with poems to traditional Burgundian melodies—and was called to trial for his trouble. This one makes demands of a singer but is well worth the effort.

English lyrics by Oscar Brand

ho - ly pres - ence warm. How man - y ox - en and
wa - ter, ate___ no food. How man - y ox - en and

don - keys now, If they were there when first___ He came,
don - keys now,___ Dressed in er - mine, silk___ and such,

How man - y ox - en and don - keys you know At such a time would
How man - y ox - en and don - keys you know At such a time would

do the same? 2. And
do as much? ( 3. As ) word.___

56

3. As soon as to these humble beasts
   Appeared our Lord, so mild and sweet,
   With joy they knelt before His Grace,
   And gently kissed His tiny feet.
   If we, like oxen and donkeys then,
   In spite of all the things we've heard,
   Would be like oxen and donkeys then,
   We'd hear the truth, believe His word.

# The Wreck of the "John B"

A theme song of the Nassau waterfront, telling the story of a little sloop and the wild party which went on the night she was sunk.

Words and music adapted by Lee Hays from a collection by Carl Sandburg

*With strong West Indian flavor*

1. We

*Verse*

come on the sloop "John B,"
first mate he got drunk,
My grand - fa - ther and me,
Broke up the peo- ple's trunk,

'Round Nas - sau town we did roam,
Con - sta - ble had to come and take him a - way,
Drink - ing all
Sher - iff John-

home, _____ Let me go home, _____ I

feel so break-up I want to go home. _____ 2. The

home. _____

# Tzena, Tzena, Tzena, Tzena

The earliest of The Weavers' hit songs, recorded with Gordon Jenkins, was learned from Israeli students visiting New York. The words mean "Come out, girls, and take a look at the soldiers in the village. Don't hide yourselves from the brave soldiers."

Music by Issachar Miron, Julius Grossman, Hebrew lyrics by Yehiel Haggiz

*Quick hora*

Tze - na, tze - na, tze - na, tze - na, Ha - ba-not ur - 'en - a cha - ya - lim _____ ba- mo-sha - va.

Al - na, al - na, al - na, al - na, Al - na tit-cha-be - na mi ben Cha - yil ish tza - va.

Tze - na, tze - na, ha - ba-not ur -'e - na Cha - ya - lim ba - mo - sha -

va. _____ Al - na, al - na, al - na, Tit - cha - be - na

mi ben Cha - yil ish tza - va.

Tze - na, tze - na Tze - na, tze - na, tze - na, Tze - na, tze - na,

# Two Brothers

This is not a folk song, but it's surely a favorite of
ours and of audiences. We doubt that even in a hundred years the folks would ever want to change a
line of it.

By Irving Gordon

One wore blue and one wore gray, As they marched a-long their way, The
can-non ball don't pay no mind If you're gen-tle or if you're kind, It

fife and drum be-gan to play, All on a beau-ti-ful morn-ing. morn-ing.
don't think of the folks be-hind,

3. Two girls waiting by the railroad track,
   Two girls waiting by the railroad track,
   Two girls waiting by the railroad track,
   One wore blue and one wore black.
   One wore blue and one wore black,
   Waiting by the railroad track
   For their darlings to come back,
   All on a beautiful morning.

# Wasn't That a Time?

Walt Whitman urged poets to write of the great events of American history. This song, using the words of Tom Paine, begins with the times that tried men's souls and carries through the wars to today and the promises of a brighter future.

By Lee Hays

*Easy march tempo*

1. Our fa - thers bled _____ at Val - ley Forge, _____ The snow was
   fought _____ at Get - tys - burg _____ Now lie in

red with blood, Their faith was warm _____ at Val - ley Forge, Their
sol - diers' graves. But there they stemmed _____ the slav - ery tide And

faith _____ was broth - er - hood. Was-n't that a time, _____ Was-n't that a
there _____ the faith was saved.

time, A time to try _____ the soul of man, Was-n't that a ter-ri-ble time! _____

2. Brave men who
(3. The Fas-cists)

**Last**

Is-n't this a won-der-ful time! _____

3. The Fascists came with chains of war
To prison us in hate.
And once again men fought and died
To save the stricken faith. *(Chorus)*

4. Our faith cries out, we have no fear,
We dare to reach our hand
To other neighbors far and near,
To friends in ev'ry land.

*Last chorus*
Isn't this a time,
Isn't this a time,
A time to free the soul of man,
Isn't this a wonderful time!
Isn't this a wonderful time!

# I Don't Want to Get Adjusted

The Weavers sing this old hymn mainly for its anti-psychiatric intent.

Traditional hymn

*With revival meeting spirit*

In this world we have our trou - bles, Some - times lone - some, some - times blue, But the hope of life e - ter - nal Bright - ens all our hopes a - new. I don't

*Chorus—Brightly, second time furiously*

want (I don't want) to get ad - just - ed _____ To this
(to get ad - just - ed)

world (to this world), to this world (to this world), I got a

home that's so much bet - ter I want to go to soon - er or

la - ter, I don't want to get ad - just - ed to this

world. _____      I   don't    world. _____

# Old Paint (Ride Around Little Dogies)

In the day of the television Western it is probably unnecessary to explain that a little "dogie" was a motherless calf; or that a "paint" was a calico horse of many colors, indicating that the parents had married for love rather than for pedigree.

Traditional

*A nice rocking tempo*

1. I ride an old paint,＿ I lead an old Dan,＿ I'm
2. Old＿ Bill Jones＿ had a daugh-ter and a son,＿ The

go-in' to Mon-tan-a to throw the hou-li-han. They
son went to col-lege and the daugh-ter went＿ wrong; His

feed in the cou-lees, they wa-ter in the draw, Their
wife got killed in a pool-room＿ fight, And

tails are all mat-ted,___ their backs are all raw.
still he keeps sing-in'___ from morn-in' to night. Ride a-

*Chorus*

round lit-tle do-gies, ride a-round ___ them ___

slow, ___ For the fier-y and snuf-fy ___ are

rar-in' to go. go.___

3. I worked in the city, worked on the farm;
   All I got to show is this muscle in my arm;
   Blisters on my feet, callus on my hands,
   And I'm goin' to Montana to throw the houlihan. *(Chorus)*


4. When I die take my saddle from the wall,
   Put it on my pony, lead him out of his stall,
   Tie my bones to his back, turn our faces to the west,
   And we'll ride the prairie that we love the best. *(Chorus)*

# Šano Dušo

This lovely Yugoslav melody should be sung flow-
ingly. The lyrics are un-self-consciously passionate—
one of the prime differences between Continental and
Anglo-American love songs.

Traditional Yugoslavian

*Translation*    1. Sano, my soul, Sano, my sea,
                   Open the door for me
                   So I can give you some coins.

               2. Night is coming, but I am so sad.
                   You are lovely—I cannot sleep.

        *Chorus*      Oh, I burn for you.
                   For you, Sano, my heart is burning.

# Talking Blues

This form is distinctly American, like all the blues, and it provides a framework for many new verses. We have heard Talking Drunk, Talking Farmer, Talking Dustbowl, Talking Union, Talking Atom.

Adaptation and arrangement by The Weavers

1. Now you wan - na go to heav - en, lem - me tell you what to do: Got - ta grease your feet in a lit - tle mut - ton stew, You just slide out ____ of the

Mom - ma's in the kitch - en pre - par - in' to eat, Sis - ter's in the pan - try look - in' for some yeast, Pa - pa's in the cel - lar

how.

3. Now they ain't no use in me workin' so hard,
   I got a gal in the rich folks' yard.
   They kill a chicken, she sends me the head.
   She thinks I'm workin', I'm layin' up in bed.
   I'm havin' a good time—
   I'm dreamin' about her—and two other women.

4. Now I took me a wife about five years ago,
   We got a little boy now just about four,
   He gets up at the table and he slaps his ma,
   Rubs syrup in my hair, and says ain't you my pa,
   Runs string beans up my nose—
   Rubs mustard in my eyes, potatoes in my ears.
   Cute kid.

5. Well, nobody likes the way I talk
   So I went out and I took a walk,
   I decided I'd go to some institution,
   Get them to teach me elocution:
   "How now, brown cow?"
   "Right now, green bull."

6. I was down in the hen house, down on my knees,
   When I thought I heard a chicken sneeze,
   But it was only the rooster sayin' his prayers,
   Thankin' the Lord for the hens upstairs.
   What with roosters a-prayin' and all the hens a-layin',
   Hm—little pullets just pluggin' away the best they know how.

# Hard Travelin'

Singers like Woody Guthrie and Cisco Houston have
done much hard travelin' from job to job, and they
know what they're singing about.

Additional words and music by Woody Guthrie

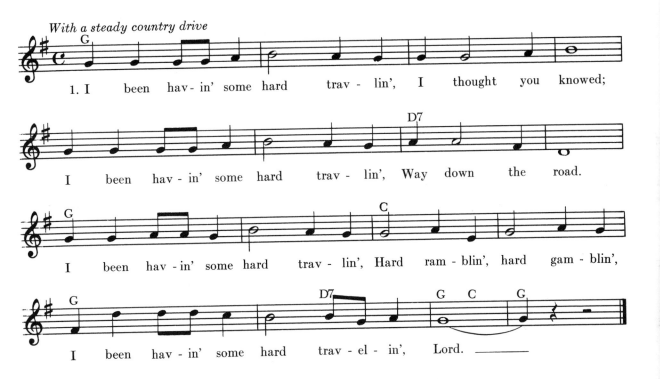

*With a steady country drive*

1. I been hav-in' some hard trav-lin', I thought you knowed;
I been hav-in' some hard trav-lin', Way down the road.
I been hav-in' some hard trav-lin', Hard ram-blin', hard gam-blin',
I been hav-in' some hard trav-el-in', Lord. _____

2. I been a-workin' in a hard rock tunnel,
I thought you knowed;
I been a-leanin' on a pressure drill,
Way down the road.
Hammer flyin', air hose suckin',
Six feet of mud, I sure been a-muckin',
I been a-havin' some hard travelin', Lord.

3. I been a-workin' that Pittsburgh steel,
I thought you knowed;
I been a-workin' that red-hot slag,
Way down the road.
I been a-blastin', I been a-firin',
I been a-duckin' red-hot iron,
I been a-havin' some hard travelin', Lord.

4. I been hittin' some hard harvestin',
I thought you knowed;
I been hittin' some rough handlin',
Way down the road.
Cut that wheat and stack that hay,
Tryin' to make about a dollar a day,
I been a-havin' some hard travelin', Lord.

5. I been a-hittin' that Lincoln Highway,
I thought you knowed;
I been a-hittin' that Sixty-six,
Way down the road.
Heavy load and a worried mind,
Lookin' for a woman that's hard to find,
I been a-havin' some hard travelin', Lord.

# Raghupati

According to Hindu mythology Ram is one of twelve incarnations of God. The first verse of this Indian song calls to Ram by several of his names and titles. The second verse says "Oh God! please give good counsel to us who may call you Eeswar and us who may call you Allah and lead us properly." Gandhi loved this song, which pleads for peace between Moslem and Hindu.

Hindu hymn, traditional

*Leader and Chorus*

Ra - ghu - pa - ti, Ra - gha - va, Ra - ja ___ Ram, ___

Pa - ti - ta Pa - ban, ___ See - ta Ram.

*Leader* *Third time repeat first verse*

1.,3. See - ta Ram jai, See - ta ___ Ram, Pa - ti - ta
2. Ees - wa - ra Al - lah te - re ___ nam Sab - ko

Chorus

Pa - ban,__ See - ta__ Ram, See - ta Ram jai,
san - mo - ti de bhag__ wan. Ees - wa - ra Al - lah

See - ta__ Ram, Pa - ti - ta Pa - ban,__ See - ta__ Ram.
te - re__ nam Sab - ko san - mo - ti de bhag - wan.

Last time

Ra - ghu - pa - ti, Ra - gha - va, Ra - ja__ Ram,_____

Pa - ti - ta Pa - ban,__ See - ta__ Ram.

# Saeynu

One of the many Israeli songs that speak of the ever-present desert, this one is sung lightly and liltingly. The "li, li, li's" of the chorus imitate the sound of camels' harness bells.

The lyrics go: "Carry us, carry us, to the desert carry us. To the desert carry us on the backs of camels. The harness bells jingle with every step."

Traditional Israeli

Sa - ey - nu, sa - ey - nu, la - mid - bar, sa - ey - nu,

Sa - ey - nu, sa - ey - nu, la - mid - bar, sa - ey - nu.

D. S. *al* FINE

hem    yets-    alt - ze - lu    pa' - am    o' ___ nim g'do - lim. ___

D. S. *al* FINE

# So Long (It's Been Good to Know Yuh)

The best-known of the many hundreds of songs written by the Oklahoma balladeer Woody Guthrie, originally it portrayed the plight of a "dust-bowl refugee," as the chorus still suggests. Woody wrote this version for The Weavers.

Words and music by Woody Guthrie

*Steadily and lustily*

1. I've sung this song, but I'll sing it a - gain, Of the peo - ple I've
sweet-hearts, they sat in the dark and they sparked, They hugged and they

met and the plac - es I've seen, Of some of the trou - bles that both- ered my
kissed in that dust - y old dark, They sighed and they cried and they hugged and they

mind, And a lot of good peo - ple that I've left be - hind, so it's:
kissed, But in - stead of mar - riage they talked like this: Hon - ey,

So long, it's been good to know yuh, So long, it's been good to know yuh, So long, it's been good to know yuh, What a long time — since I've been home, And I got to be drift-ing a-long. 2.The long.

3. I went to your family and asked them for you,
   They all said take her, oh, take her, please do!
   She can't cook or sew and she won't scrub your floor,
   So I put on my hat and tiptoed out the door, saying: *(Chorus)*


4. I walked down the street to the grocery store,
   It was crowded with people both rich and both poor.
   I asked the man how his butter was sold,
   He said: One pound of butter for two pounds of gold, I said: *(Chorus)*


5. My telephone rang and it jumped off the wall,
   That was the preacher a-making a call,
   He said: We're waiting to tie the knot,
   You're getting married, believe it or not!


6. The church it was jammed, the church it was packed,
   The pews were crowded from the front to the back,
   A thousand friends waited to kiss my new bride,
   But I was so anxious I rushed her outside, told them: *(Chorus)*

# The Boll Weevil

This is an Arkansas version of the ballad of the industrious *Anthonomus grandis* which once nearly ate up the South. In one town there is a statue of the boll weevil, which destroyed the cotton crop and forced the farmers to turn to diversified farming.

Additional words and music arrangement by Lee Hays

1. Well, the first time I saw the boll wee-vil,__ He was a-stand-in' on the square.
boll wee-vil said to his ev-er-lov-in'wife, "Hon-ey, get up and stand on your two big feet.__ Take a look o-ver yon-der in Ar-kan-sas At all the whole durn fam-'ly there. They were look-in'for a home, They were look-in'for a
cot-ton we've got to eat.__ We'll have a home, We'll have a
They were look-in'for a home,

The next time I saw the boll wee-vil,__ He had his

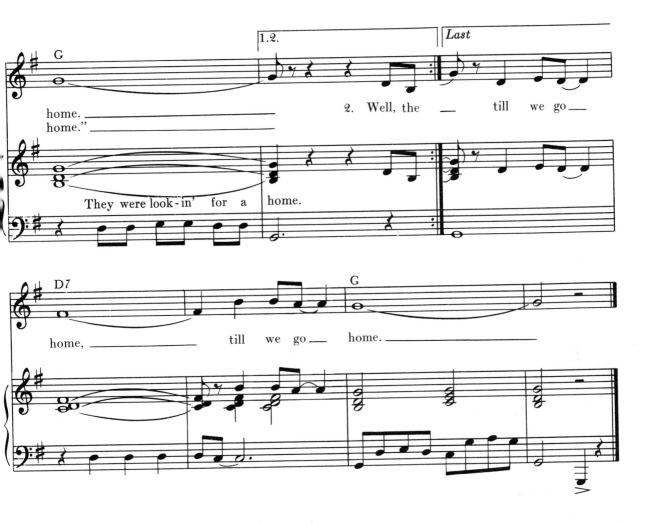

3. Well, the farmer took the boll weevil,
   Put him in a cake of ice.
   Boll weevil said to the farmer,
   "This is mighty cool and nice,
   It'll be my home, it'll be my home."

4. The boll weevil said to the lightnin' bug,
   "Can I get up a little bit of a deal with you?
   If I was a lightnin' bug,
   I'd be workin' the whole night through,
   I'd have me a home, I'd have me a home."

5. The boll weevil ate up half the cotton,
   The banker stole the rest.
   Didn't leave that poor old farmer's wife
   But a poor old raggedy dress;
   It's full of holes, it's full of holes.

6. Now, if anybody should ask you
   Who it was that sang this song,
   Tell him it was four singin' Weavers,
   And we can sing it all night long,
   Till we go home, till we go home.

# This Land Is Your Land

Woody Guthrie wrote this as a love song to America,
and many think it is his finest effort.

Words and music by Woody Guthrie

*Simply and with dignity*

This land is your _____ land, this land is my land, _____ From Cal - i - for - nia _____ to the New York Is - land, _____ From the red - wood for - est _____ to the Gulf Stream wa - ter, _____

*Last time*

This land was made for you and me._____ 1. As I went
2. I roamed and I

walk - ing _____ that rib-bon of high - way, _____ I saw a -
ram - bled _____ and I fol-lowed my foot - steps _____ To the spar - kling

bove me _____ that end - less sky - way, _____ I saw be -
sands of _____ her dia - mond des - erts, _____ While all a -

low me _____ that gold - en val - ley, _____ Say - ing,
round me _____ a voice was sound - ing, _____

This land was made for you and me. _____

"This land was made for you and me." _____ This land is

me _____ This land was made for you and

me. _____

3. The sun came shining and I was strolling,
   And the wheat fields waving and the dust clouds rolling,
   As the fog was lifting, a voice was chanting,
   "This land was made for you and me."

# The Johnson Boys

A guitar or banjo used to be mighty handy when a
fellow courted a girl, and probably still is. In this silly
song, the girls get a chance to poke fun at the boys.

*Like a mountain dance tune*

Additional words and music arrangement by The Weavers

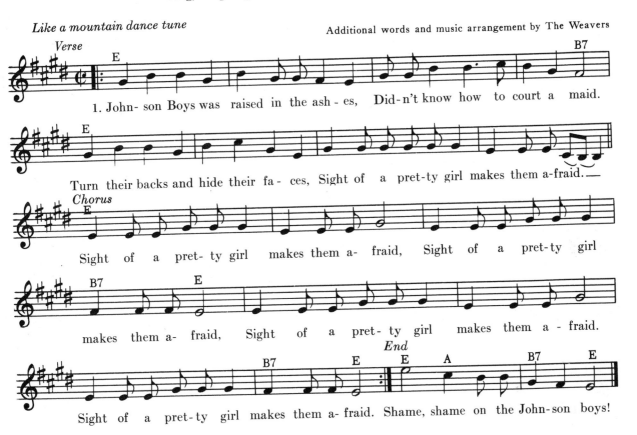

1. John-son Boys was raised in the ash-es, Did-n't know how to court a maid.
Turn their backs and hide their fa-ces, Sight of a pret-ty girl makes them a-fraid. —

*Chorus*
Sight of a pret-ty girl makes them a-fraid, Sight of a pret-ty girl
makes them a-fraid, Sight of a pret-ty girl makes them a-fraid.
Sight of a pret-ty girl makes them a-fraid. Shame, shame on the John-son boys!

2. Johnson Boys, they come a-courtin'
   The Coon Creek girls so pretty and sweet,
   They couldn't make no conversation,
   They didn't know where to put their feet.
   *Chorus:* They didn't know where to put their feet, *(four times)*

3. Johnson Boys, they went a-courtin',
   Ridin' in a Chevrolet,
   They come home broke and walkin',
   Had no money for to pay their way.
   *Chorus:* Had no money for to pay their way, *(four times)*

4. Johnson Boys eat peas and honey,
   They have done it all of their life;
   Makes the peas taste mighty funny,
   But it keeps them on the knife.
   *Chorus:* But it keeps them on the knife, *(four times)*

5. Johnson Boys'll never get married,
   They'll live single all of their life,
   They're too scared to pop the question,
   There ain't no woman that'll be their wife.
   *Chorus:* There ain't no woman that'll be their wife, *(four times)*

# Die Gedanken Sind Frei

Sung in Hesse in 1800, this became a favorite of German youth groups in the 1930's, when Hilda Kevass learned and sang it. Later, her husband, Arthur, wrote the English words.

One hundred sixty years after it was first sung there are still places where it might be sung as if it had just been written.

German folk song. English translation by Arthur Kevass

1.
Die Ge-dank - en sind — frei, My thoughts free - ly flow - er; Die Ge-
Die Ge-dank - en sind — frei, Wer kann sie er - rat - en; Sie

dank - en sind — frei, My thoughts give me pow - er; No schol - ar can
flieh - en vor - bei, Wie nächt - lich - e Schat - ten; Kein Mensch kann sie

map them, No hunt - er can trap them, No man can — de - ny, Die Ge-
wis - sen Kein Jä - ger er - schies-sen, Es bleib- et — da - bei, Die Ge-

dank - en  sind  frei,  No  man can de - ny, ___ Die Ge-dank- en  sind frei.
dank - en  sind  frei,  Es  bleib- et  da - bei, ___ Die Ge-dank- en  sind frei.

2. So I think as I please,
   And this gives me pleasure;
   My conscience decrees
   This right I must treasure;
   My thoughts will not·cater
   To duke or dictator;
   No man can deny
   Die Gedanken sind frei! } repeat

   Ich denke was ich will,
   Und was mich beglücket,
   Doch alles in der Still,
   Und wie es sich schicket.
   Mein Wunsch und Begehren
   Kann niemand verwehren
   Es bleibet dabei:
   Die Gedanken sind frei! } repeat

3. And if tyrants take me
   And throw me in prison,
   My thoughts will burst free,
   Like blossoms in season.
   Foundations will crumble,
   The structure will tumble,
   And free men will cry
   Die Gedanken sind frei! } repeat

   Und sperrt man mich ein
   Im finsteren Kerker,
   Das alles sind rein,
   Vergebliche Werke;
   Denn meine Gedanken
   Zerreissen die Schranken
   Und Mauern entzwei:
   Die Gedanken sind frei! } repeat

# Jig Along Home

A new children's song by the writer of many a song
for his own children, Woody Guthrie.

Words and music by Woody Guthrie

1. I went to a dance and the an-i-mals come; The jay-bird danced with
   fish did a dance to the fish-ing reel, The lob-ster danced on the

horse-shoes on, The grass-hop-per danced till he fell on the floor!
pea-cock's tail, The ba-boon danced with the ris-ing moon,

Jig a-long, jig a-long, jig a-long home.
Jig a-long, jig a-long, jig a-long home. Jig jig-a jig jig-a jig a-long home,

Jig jig-a jig jig-a jig a-long home, Jig a-long, jig a-long, jig a-long home,

Jig jig-a jig jig-a jig a-long home. 2.The jig a-long home. —

3. Mama rat took off her hat,
   Shook the house with the old tom cat,
   The alligator beat his tail on the drum,
   Jig along, jig along, jig along home. *(Chorus)*

4. The boards did rattle and the house did shake,
   The clouds did laugh and the world did quake,
   New moon rattled some silver spoons,
   Jig along, jig along, jig along home. *(Chorus)*

5. The nails flew loose and the floor broke down,
   Everybody danced around and around,
   The house come down, the crowd went home,
   Jig along, jig along, jig along home. *(Chorus)*

# (Come On and) Join into the Game

Even the littlest kids can join in this song, with actions
and noises to suit the words.

Additional words and music adaptation by Paul Campbell (The Weavers)

*Swinging*

1. Let eve-ry-one clap hands like me, *(clap hands)* Let eve-ry-one clap hands like me. *(clap hands)* Come on and join in-to the game; You'll find that it's al-ways the same. *(clap hands)* 2. Let

2. Let everyone whistle like me, *(whistle)*
   Let everyone whistle like me. *(whistle)*
   Come on and join into the game;
   You'll find that it's always the same. *(whistle)*

3. Let everyone laugh like me, *(laugh)*
   *(continue as in previous verses)*

4. Let everyone sneeze like me, *(sneeze)*
   *(continue as in previous verses)*

5. Let everyone yawn like me, *(yawn)*
   *(continue as in previous verses)*

6. Let everyone do what he wants, *(various sounds)*
   *(continue as in previous verses)*

# Aunt Rhody

It would be impossible to say how many generations of babies have been sung to sleep with this song. Scholars say it came from old France; some say the philosopher Rousseau had a hand in its making.

Traditional

*Steady and relaxed*

1. Go tell Aunt Rho - dy, Go tell Aunt Rho - dy,

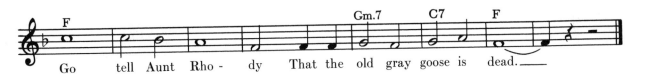

Go tell Aunt Rho - dy That the old gray goose is dead.___

2. The one she's been saving, *(three times)*
   To make a feather bed.

3. The old gander's weeping, *(three times)*
   Because his wife is dead.

4. The goslings are mourning, *(three times)*
   Because their mother's dead.

5. She died in the mill pond, *(three times)*
   From standing on her head.

6. Go tell Aunt Rhody, *(three times)*
   That the old gray goose is dead.

# Poor Howard

Another one of the countless hoedowns, with countless verses—to be improvised as the occasion suggests.

Adaptation and arrangement by The Weavers

*Opening Chorus*

Poor How - ard's dead and gone, Left me here to sing this song,

Poor How - ard's dead and gone, Left me here to sing this song.

Poor How - ard's dead and he's gone, Poor How - ard's dead and he's gone, Oh___

poor How - ard's dead and he's gone, Left me here to sing this song.

*Verses 1. 2. 3.*

1. Who's been here since I've been gone? Great big man with a der - by on.

Who's been here since I've been gone? Great big man with a der - by on.

Great big man with a der - by on,___ Great big man with a der - by

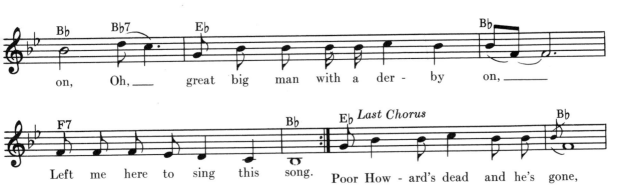

on, Oh, ___ great big man with a der - by on, _____

Left me here to sing this song. Poor How - ard's dead and he's gone,

*Last Chorus*

Poor How - ard's dead and he's gone, Oh___ Poor How - ard's dead and he's

gone, Left me here to sing this song.

2. Who's been here since I've been gone?
   Pretty little girl with the red dress on.
   Who's been here since I've been gone?
   Pretty little girl with the red dress on.
   Pretty little girl with the red dress on,
   Pretty little girl with the red dress on, .
   Oh, pretty little girl with the red dress on,
   Left me here to sing this song. *(Chorus)*

3. How I wish that train would come,
   Take me back where I come from.
   How I wish that train would come,
   Take me back where I come from.
   How I wish that train would come,
   How I wish that train would come,
   How I wish that train would come,
   Take me back where I come from. *(Last chorus)*

# The Wild Goose Grasses (Tarrytown)

The ageless tale, retold to a lovely melody, of the girl
who loved too well, too much, and too soon.

Words and music by John Allison

*Simply and tenderly*

1. In Tarry-town there did dwell
   wore my apron low,

A handsome youth, I loved him well;
He followed me through ice and snow;

He courted me, my life away,
Now that I wear my apron high,

But now with me he will no long-er stay. Wide and
He goes right down my street and pass-es by.

*Chorus*

deep _____ my grave will be, _____ With the

wild goose grass-es grow-in' o-ver me. _____ Wide and deep _____

_____ my grave will be, _____ With the wild goose grass-es

grow - in' o - ver me. _____ 2. When I me. _____

3. There is an inn in Tarrytown,
   Where my love goes and sits him down;
   He takes another on his knee,
   For she has gold and riches more than me.

# Kum Bachur Atzel

The words of this Hebrew round, long a campfire
favorite, are very easy to learn. They say: "The
cuckoo rises and sings 'Cuckoo.'"

Arranged and adapted by Erik Darling, Lee Hays, Fred Hellerman and Ronnie Gilbert

Kum ba-chur at - zel, ___ V' tze l' a - vo - da.

Kum ba-chur at - zel, ___ V' tze l' a - vo - da.

Kum, kum, ___ V' tze l' a - vo - da. Kum, kum, ___ V'

tze l' a - vo - da. Cu - cu - ri - cu, Cu - cu - ri - cu, Tar - n' gol ka -

ra, Cu - cu - ri - cu, Cu - cu - ri - cu, Tar - n' gol ka - ra.

# The Midnight Special

Leadbelly told of a prison legend of the midnight train running past; if the headlight should shine through the bars of the cell, it was a sign that the prisoner would soon go free.

Traditional

One day, one day, ___ I was walk-in' a-long. ___

I heard the Mid-night ___ Spe-cial ___ Sing-in' a lone-some song. ___

___ Oh, let the Mid-night Spe-cial ___ Shine her light on

Well, it's a-set-tin' on the table, ___ A knife, a fork and a
Be-cause the sher-iff will ar-rest you; ___ He's gon-na take ___ you

pan. If you say an-y-thing a-bout it, ___
down. And you can bet your bot-tom dol-lar ___

You're ___ in trou-ble with the man. Oh, let the Mid-night
You're pen-i-ten-tiar-y bound. ___

Shine her ev-er-lov-in' light on me. ___

3. Well, yonder comes Miss Rosie.
   Tell me, how did you know?
   I knew by the color of her apron
   And the dress she wore.
   Well, she brought me a little coffee
   And she brought me a little tea.
   Well, she brought me nearly ev'rything
   Except the jailhouse key! *(Chorus)*

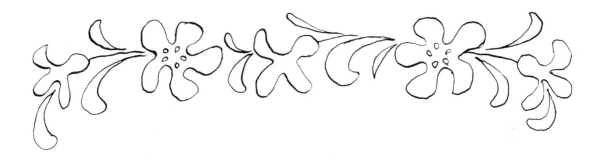

# Every Night When the Sun Goes Down

One of the classics of the American folk song.

Traditional. Arranged by Fred Hellerman

3. I wish the Lord my train would come,
   I wish the Lord my train would come,
   I wish the Lord my train would come,
   And take me back where I come from.

4. I wish the Lord my babe was born
   Sittin' on his daddy's knee,
   And me, poor girl, was dead and gone
   With green grass growin' over me.

5. *(Same as first verse)*

# Bury Me Beneath the Willow

Don't be misled by the words into making a
dirge of this one. Just sing them straightfor-
wardly, and go along with the tune, which is
lively, even rousing, in the best "blue-grass"
tradition.

Traditional

*Opening Chorus — Unnecessarily loud and fast*

Bu - ry me be - neath the wil - low, 'Neath the weep-ing wil - low tree.

When he hears that _ I am sleep-ing May - be then he'll think of me. 1. My

*Verse*

heart is sad and _ I am lone-ly, Think-ing of the one I love. When

will I see him? _ Oh, no, nev-er, Un - less we meet in heav'n a - bove.

*Chorus*

Bu - ry me be - neath the wil - low, 'Neath the weep-ing wil- low tree.

When he hears that _ I am sleep-ing May - be then he'll think of me. 2.(She) me.

2. She told me that she dearly loved me.
   How could I believe 'r untrue?
   Until one day some neighbors told me,
   "She has proven untrue to you." *(Chorus)*

3. Tomorrow was to be our wedding;
   I pray, oh, Lord, where can he be?
   He's gone, he's gone to love another;
   He no longer cares for me. *(Chorus)*

# Sylvie

After Leadbelly sang a few lines of this song
for The Weavers years ago, the tune and the
idea were impossible to put aside, so we added
a few verses and the "release" to make it into
a whole song.

Words and music by Huddie Ledbetter and Paul Campbell (The Weavers)

# Done Laid Around

Who hasn't heard that lonesome whistle blow and felt,
like the guy in the song, that it's time to travel on?

New words and music by Paul Clayton, Larry Ehrlich, David Lazar, Paul Six

Done laid a-round, done stayed a-round This old town too long;

Sum-mer's al-most gone, sum-mer's al-most gone.

Done laid a-round, done stayed a-round This old\_ town too long, And I
feel like I want to trav-el on._____

*Last time To Coda*

1. There's a
2. The

lone-some freight at six-oh-eight Com-in' through\_ the town,
chil-ly\_ wind will soon be-gin;\_ I'll be on my way,

I'll be home-ward bound, I'll be home-ward bound, A
Gone a lone-some day, go-in' home to stay. The

lone - some freight at six- oh - eight Com- in' through the town And I
chil-ly wind will soon be - gin;— I'll be on my way, And I

Am. D7 G Coda G

feel like I want to trav-el on._____ on. _____
feel like I want to trav-el on._____

Coda

3. I've waited here for most a year,
   Waiting for the sun to shine,
   Waiting for the sun to shine, hoping you'd change your mind.
   I've waited here for most a year,
   Hoping you'd change your mind;
   Now I feel like I want to travel on.

# Eres Alta

A love song from Spain, learned from the singing of
Germaine Montero.

Traditional Spanish folk song

*Moderately*

*Verse*

1. E - res al - ta y del - ga - da Co - mo tu ma - dre, Mo - re - na y sal - a -
2. E - res co - mo la ro - sa de A - le - jan - drí - a, Mo - re - na y sal - a -

da, Co - mo tu ma - dre. Ben - di - ta sea la - ra - ma
da, De A - le - jan - drí - a, Co - lo - ra - da de no - che,

que al tron-co sa - le, Mo-re-na y sal-a-da, Que al-tron-co sa___ le.
blan-ca de dí - a, Mo-re-na y sal-a-da, Blan-ca de dí___ a.

*Chorus*
(C bass)

To - da la no-che es-toy, _____ Ni ___ ña, pen-san-do en tí ___

___ Que yo de a-mo-res me mue-ro des-de que te

ví, Mo-re-na y sal-a-da, des-de que te ___ ví.

*Translation*  1. You are tall and slender,
      Like your mother, Dark-and-Graceful.
      Bless the branch
      That goes forth from the trunk!

2. You are like the Rose of Alexandria,
      Graceful brunette,
      Scarlet by night
      And white by day.

*Chorus*     All through the night, little one,
      I think about you;
      Love is killing me,
      I am dying of love since I saw you.

# You Old Fool

Emma Dusenberry, the blind singer in the Ozarks,
taught this song to Lee Hays. In its present form it
has become somewhat citified.

New words and new music arrangement by Lee Hays, Fred Hellerman, Ronnie Gilbert

*Boy*

1. I came home the oth-er night as drunk as I could be; I
saw a horse in the sta-ble where my horse ought to be. I
said to my wife, my pret-ty lit-tle wife, "Ex-plain this thing to me, What's this
horse do-ing here in the sta-ble where my horse ought to be?" *Girl* "Well, you
old fool, you blind fool, Can't you plain-ly see? It's
*Boy* noth-ing but a milk cow that my moth-er sent to me." I've
tra-veled this wide world o-ver, ten thou-sand miles or more, But a

sad-dle and a bri-dle on a milk cow I nev-er did see be-fore, A

sad-dle and a bri-dle on a milk cow I ne-ver did see be-fore.

2. I came home the next night so drunk I could not see,
   And there was a hat on the hatrack where my hat ought to be.
   I said to my wife, my pretty little wife, "Explain this thing to me,
   What's this hat doing on the hatrack where my hat ought to be?"
          "Oh, you old fool, you blind fool,
              Can't you plainly see?
              It's nothing but a chamberpot
              My mother sent to me."
   I've traveled this wide world over, ten thousand miles or more,
   But a J. B. Stetson chamberpot I never did see before,
   But a J.B. Stetson chamberpot I never did see before.

3. I came home the next night as drunk as I could be;
   I saw some pants upon the chair where my pants ought to be.
   Well, I said to my wife, my pretty little wife, "Explain this thing to me,
   What's these pants doing on the chair where my pants ought to be?"
          "Oh, you old fool, you blind fool,
              Can't you plainly see?
              It's nothing but a dish-rag
              My mother sent to me."
   I've traveled this wide world over, ten thousand miles or more,
   But cuffs and a zipper on a dish-rag I never did see before,
   But cuffs and a zipper on a dish-rag I never did see before.

4. I came home the next night as drunk as I could be,
   And there was a head on the pillow where my head ought to be.
   I said to my wife, my pretty little wife, "Explain this thing to me,
   What's this head doing here on the pillowcase where my head ought to be?"
          "You old fool, you blind fool,
              Can't you plainly see?
              It's nothing but a melon
              My mother sent to me."
   I've traveled this wide world over, ten thousand miles or more,
   But a mustache on a mushmelon I never did see before,
   But a mustache on a mushmelon I never did see before.

   (Spoken:) It's a good thing I'm not of a suspicious nature . . . .

# Eddystone Light

There is less to this song than meets the ear sometimes. It's just for fun.

Arranged and adapted, new words by Fred Hellerman

*As a hornpipe*

1. My

fa - ther was the keep- er  of  the Ed - dy-stone Light, He court-ed  a mer - maid
what has  be - come of  my chil- dren three?" My moth-er____ then she

one fine night. From this  u - ni - on  there came three:  A
asked of me. "One was ex - hib- it -ed  as a  talk - ing fish, And the

por- poise and a por- gy and the oth- er was me. Yo - ho - ho, the
oth- er was served on a chaf- ing dish." 

wind blows free, Oh, for a life on the roll - ing sea._____ One
Then the

night while I was trim-min' of the glim, Sing - in' the verse of the
phos-pho - rus flashed in her sea - weed hair, I looked a - gain, my

eve - ning hymn, A voice from the star - board shout - ed, "A - hoy!" And
moth- er was- n't there. A voice came e - cho- in' out of the night, "To the

there was me moth-er a - sit-tin' on a buoy. *Don't be ri - dic - u - lous.

devil with the keep-er of the Ed- dy- stone Light!" *A boy is a ju - ve - nile male.* No, a

buoy, *it guides the ships to sail.* 2. "Tell me

Yo - ho - ho, the wind blows free, Oh, for a life on the

roll - - - ing sea. _____

# Greenland Whale Fisheries

Pete Seeger and Fred Hellerman joined the old New
England ballad with a Bahaman fragment to drama-
tize the story of life on whaling vessels.

Adapted and arranged by Fred Hellerman.

When the whale gets strike and the line run 'round, And the whale makes a flun-der with its tail, And the boat cap-sized and I lost my dar-lin' man, No more, no more Green-land for you, brave

boys, No more, no more Green-land for you. 1. 'Twas in

**March tempo**

eight - een hun - dred and fif - ty - three, Of June the thir - teenth
look - out on __ the __ cross - tree stood With a spy - glass in __ his __

day, That our gal - lant ship her __ an - chor __ weighed And for
hand. "There's a whale, there's a whale, there's a whale __ fish," he cried. "She __

Green - land sailed __ a - way, brave boys, and for
blows out ev - 'ry __ span, brave boys, she __

Green - land sailed ___ a - way.
blows out ev - 'ry span."

1.2.

2. The

Last D. C. al FINE

seen.

D. C. al FINE

3. We struck that whale and the line paid out,
   But she made a flunder with her tail,
   And the boat capsized and four men were drowned,
   And we never caught that whale, brave boys, we never caught that whale.

4. "To lose the whale," the captain said,
   "It grieves my heart full sore,
   But to lose four of my gallant men
   It grieves me ten times more, brave boys, it grieves me ten times more."

5. Oh, Greenland is a dreadful place,
   A land that's never green,
   Where there's ice and snow and the whale fishes blow,
   And daylight's seldom seen, brave boys, and daylight's seldom seen.

# Si Me Quieres Escribir

As World War II was beginning in Spain, we began to hear and sing songs from that conflict. This one, to the melody of an an- cient dance tune, is typical of soldiers' songs throughout history; the lyric is at once a gripe, a boast and a challenge.

*Con fuego*

Traditional, as sung by Spanish Republican Army

2. Si tu quieres comer bien,
   Barato y de buena forma, } *(repeat)*
   En el frente de Gandeza
   Allí tienen una fonda. } *(repeat)*

3. En la entrada de la fonda
   Hay un moro, Mojamed, } *(repeat)*
   Que se dice, "Paysa, Paysa,
   Qué quieres para comer?" } *(repeat)*

4. El primer plato que dan
   Son granadas rompedoras, } *(repeat)*
   El segundo, de metralla,
   Para recordar memorias. } *(repeat)*

*Translation*

1. If you want to write to me,
   You know my address:
   Gandeza Front,
   First Line of Fire.

2. If you want to eat
   Well and cheaply,
   At Gandeza Front
   There's an inn.

3. At the entrance
   There's a Moor, Mohammed,
   Who says, "Come in! Come in!
   What would you like to eat?"

4. The first dish they give you
   Is exploding hand grenades,
   The second,
   Bullets, to awaken memories.

# Nobody Knows You When You're Down and Out

There are times when life's so full of troubles it
seems the only thing left to do is sit back and yell
at it. . . .

By Jimmy Cox

*Medium blues*

Once I lived the life of a mil-lion-aire,— Spend-in' my mon-ey— and I did-n't care,— Tak-in' my friends out— for a might-y good time,— Buy-in' high-priced li-quor,— cham-pagne— and wine. But then I be-gan to

In your pock - et not __ one pen - ny, __ And when it comes __ to friends,

you have-n't an - y. __ But when you get back __ on your feet a - gain, __

Eve - ry - bod - y wants to be your long -lost friend. __ Well, it's might - y strange,

with- out a doubt, __ No - bod - y knows you when you're down __ and out, __

Down — and out,     oh, —     when you're down  and out. —

# The Devil and the Farmer's Wife

From a Southern version of the old Scottish ballad,
set up for the whole crowd to sing.

Traditional

*Like a community sing*

The de - vil he come to the farm - er one day, Tee - roo, tee -

roo, to the farm - er one day, Says, "One of your fam' - ly I'm

tak - in' a - way, Tee - roo, tee - roo, I'm tak - in' a - way."

2. "Oh, please don't take my eldest son,
   Teeroo, teeroo, my eldest son,
   There's work on the farm that's got to be done,
   Teeroo, teeroo, that's got to be done."

3. "Take my wife, take my wife with the joy of my heart,
   Teeroo, teeroo, with the joy of my heart,
   And I hope, by golly, that you never part,
   Teeroo, teeroo, that you never part."

4. The Devil put the old lady into a sack,
   Teeroo, teeroo, into a sack,
   And down the road he goes clickety-clack,
   Teeroo, teeroo, goes clickety-clack.

5. When the Devil got her to the fork of the road,
   Teeroo, teeroo, to the fork of the road,
   He says, "Old woman, you're a hell of a load,
   Teeroo, teeroo, you're a hell of a load."

6. When the Devil got her to the gates of Hell,
   Teeroo, teeroo, to the gates of Hell,
   He says, "Poke up the fires, we'll bake her well,
   Teeroo, teeroo, we'll bake her well."

7. Up came a little devil with a ball and chain,
   Teeroo, teeroo, with a ball and chain,
   She upped with her foot and she kicked out his brains,
   Teeroo, teeroo, she kicked out his brains.

8. Then nine little devils went climbing the wall,
   Teeroo, teeroo, went climbing the wall,
   Screaming, "Take her back, Daddy, she'll murder us all,
   Teeroo, teeroo, she'll murder us all."

9. The old man was peeping out of the crack,
   Teeroo, teeroo, peeping out of the crack,
   When he saw the old devil come bring her back,
   Teeroo, teeroo, come bringing her back.

10. He says,"Here's your wife both sound and well,
    Teeroo, teeroo, both sound and well,
    If I kept her there longer she'd have torn up Hell,
    Teeroo, teeroo, she'd have torn up Hell."

11. He says, "I've been a devil most all of my life,
    Teeroo, teeroo, most all of my life,
    But I've never been in Hell till I met with your wife,
    Teeroo, teeroo, till I met with your wife."

12. This proves that the women are better than the men,
    Teeroo, teeroo, are better than the men,
    They can all go to Hell and come back again,
    Teeroo, teeroo, and come back again.

# Hopsha Diri

This song from Yugoslavia is fun to do if you enjoy the Bathtub School of singing. You take lots of breath after each line of the verses so you can sing the next line at top volume, letting the pear-shaped tones ring out and bounce back at you, to delight your ear.

(Then for relief, sing the choruses in tempo and rather quickly.) The words are: "My sweetheart's hedges are green. Across the Morave River a girl is reading a newspaper. That bent old woman wishes she had a husband."

Traditional Yugoslavian

Hop - sha di - ri dir di - ri dir, Hop - sha da - ra da - da - da.

Hop - sha di - ri di - ri - di - ri - di - ri, Hop - sha da - ra da - ra - da - ra - da,

Hop - sha di - ri dir di - ri dir, Hop - sha da - ra da - da - da.

3. Jedna baba grbava
   Rado bi se udala
   Rado bi se udala
   Jedna baba grbava.

# House of the Rising Sun

In New Orleans, some say, they can show you where the "house" stood, where many a poor girl tried her play and lost. The sign of the rising sun was simply a red lantern.

Adaptation and arrangement by Fred Hellerman and Ronnie Gilbert

man - y _ a poor _ girl, And me, oh, God, _____ was
sat - is - fied was when he drank his li - quor _

**1, 2.**

one. _____ 2. My

down.

3. Now the only thing a gambling man needs
   Is a suitcase and a trunk;
   And the only time he's ever satisfied
   Is when he's on a drunk.

4. Go and tell my baby sister
   Never do like I have done,
   But to shun that house in New Orleans
   That they call the Rising Sun.

5. I'm going back to New Orleans;
   My race is almost run;
   I'm going back to spend the rest of my life
   Beneath that Rising Sun.

# Old Riley

All too seldom, a man gets away from prison. If he is
lucky, like Riley, he gets across the river where Rattler,
the bloodhound, can't catch him.

Adaptation and arrangement by Paul Campbell (The Weavers) and Joel Newman (Huddie Ledbetter)

(Chorus)

ad lib.

Old Ri - ley crossed the wa - - - - - -

ter, Old Ri - ley crossed the wa - - - - -

ter, On them long hot sum - mer days. ____

Verse

2. He's

1. Rat - tler, Rat - ler, there's a pris - on - er gone, __ Here, Rat - tler,
head - ed for the riv - er just as sure as you're born, __ Here, Rat - tler,

here. He's head - ed for the riv - er just as sure as you're born. __
here. I can hear that ser - geant blow-in' his horn. __

Here, Rat - tler, here. Here, Old Rat - tler, __ here, Rat - tler,
Hear, Rat - tler, here. Here, Old Rat - tler, __ here, Rat - tler,

here, Here, Old Rat - tler, __ here, Rat - tler, here.
here, Here, Old Rat - tler, __ here, Rat - tler, here.

3. He's headed to the North where you can't go.
   Here, Rattler, here.
   He's headed to the North to freedom land.
   Here, Rattler, here.
   Here, Old Rattler, here, Rattler, here,
   Here, Old Rattler, here, Rattler, here.

4. Ol' Beatum, Ol' Feedum, Ol' Cheatum done gone.
   Here, Rattler, here.
   Ol' Beatum, Ol' Feedum, Ol' Cheatum done gone.
   Here, Rattler, here.
   Here, Old Rattler, here, Rattler, here,
   Here, Old Rattler, here, Rattler, here.

# State of Arkansas

Mrs. Emma Dusenberry, a blind folk-singer of the Ozarks, was a neighbor of Lee Hays, to whom she taught this song. The tune is closely related to "the great American melody," that ballad tune sometimes heard as "Acres of Clams," "Lincoln and Liberty," and probably dozens of others.

*Additional words by Lee Hays*

*Moderately*

1. My name is Char - lie Brenn - an; _____ from
dodge be - hind the de - pot _____ To

Charles - ton I come. I've trav-eled this wide world
dodge that bliz - zard wind. I met a walk - ing

o - ver, _____ Some ups and downs I've had;
skel - e - ton, _____ He said his name was Thom - as Quinn.

I've trav-eled this wide world o - ver, _____ Some
Well, his hair hung down in rat - tails _____ On his

ups and downs I've saw, _____ But I nev-er real-ly knew what
lean and lan - tern jaw; _____ He in - vit - ed me to

*Last time Coda* ⊕

mis - 'ry was, _____ Till I hit old Ar - kan-
his ho - tel, _____ He said it was the best in Ar - kan-

1.
sas. _____ *Spoken* *I got off the train in Little Rock in the middle*
*of winter. Nobody there to extend me his paw*
*nor bid me welcome to the State of Arkansas. And it was cold.*
2. I

(repeat vamp until speech is finished.)

143

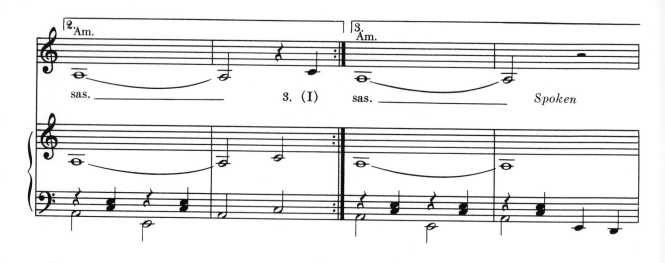

3. (I) sas. _____ *Spoken*

*Then I went out and got me a job on a farm—farmin'. But I didn't care for the work—or the farmer—or his wife and none of his children. So I went up to him one day and I said, "Mister, I'm gonna quit this job and you can just pay me off right now." He says, "O.K., son, if that's the way you feel about it," and he took me out in the barn and he handed me a mink skin. I said, "I don't want this thing, I want my money for the work I've done." He says, "Son, ya may not know it, but mink skins is what we're usin' for currency down here now." So I took it—went into town —hunted up a place—put my mink skin upon the counter, and durned if the bartender didn't toss me a pint. Then he picked up my mink skin—blowed the hair back on it—put it under the counter—fetched me out fourteen rabbit skins and three 'possum hides for change.*

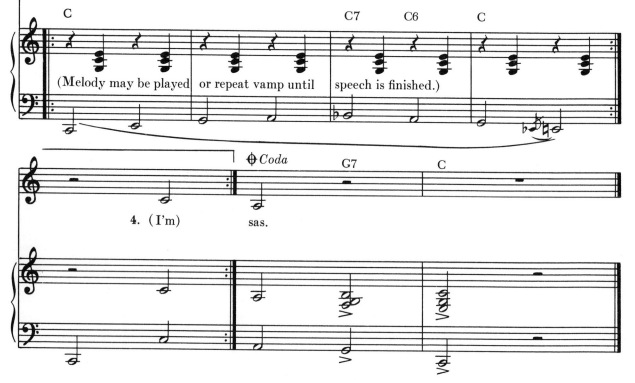

(Melody may be played    or repeat vamp until    speech is finished.)

4. (I'm)    sas.

3. I followed my conductor
   To his respected place,
   Where pity and starvation
   Were to be seen on ev'ry face.
   Well, his bread it was corn dodger,
   And his meat I could not chaw,
   But he charged me a half a dollar
   In the State of Arkansas.

4. I'm goin' to the Indian Territory
   And live outside the law.
   I'll bid farewell to the canebrakes
   In the State of Arkansas.
   If you ever see me back again,
   I'll extend to you my paw,
   But it'll be through a telescope
   From Hell to Arkansas.

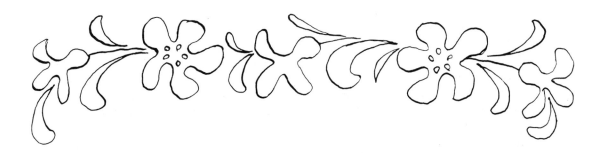

# Mi Caballo Blanco

A cowboy song from Chile.

By Francisco Flores Del Campo; arranged and adapted by
Erik Darling, Ronnie Gilbert, Lee Hays and Fred Hellerman

Galopando va, ____ Mi caballo, mi caballo,

Se va y se va. Ah ____

Hum ____

3. Al Taita Dios le pido,
   Y Él lo sabe muy bien
   Si a Su lado me llama,
   En mi caballo iré. *(Chorus)*

*Translation*  1. My horse is fair as the dawn.
                  Always we go together;
                  He's my most faithful friend.
                  Galloping, he goes and goes.

               2. On wings of joy my horse runs—
                  And on wings of sorrow, too,
                  He carries me.

               3. I pray to God, and well He knows,
                  If He calls me to His side,
                  On my horse I will go.

# The Keeper

This one started out in the days of Robin Hood, probably, and has been sung at many a campfire since then. In the original the keeper hunted down the deer and killed her; in our version we felt sorry for the poor doe and in our last verse we arranged to let her go.

Additional words and music arranged by
Ronnie Gilbert, Lee Hays and Fred Hellerman

*A good bright tempo*

1. The

*Verse*

keep - er did a - hunt - ing go, Un-der his cloak he car-ried a bow,
first doe she did cross the plain, The keep - er fetched her back a - gain.

All for to shoot a mer-ry lit - tle doe A - mong the leaves so green - o.
Where she is now she may re - main, A - mong the leaves so green - o.

**Chorus**

Jack - ie boy (Mas - ter), Sing ye well (Ver - y well), Hey down (Ho down),

Der - ry der - ry down, A - mong the leaves so green - o To my hey down down (to my

Hey down der - ry der - ry down, A - mong the leaves so ho down down), (ho down),

green - o. 2. The green - o.

3. The next doe she did cross the brook.
   The keeper fetched her back with his hook.
   Where she is now you may go and look
   Among the leaves so green-o. *(Chorus)*

4. The keeper did a-hunting go.
   In the woods he caught a doe.
   She looked so sad that he had to let her go
   Among the leaves so green-o. *(Repeat chorus twice)*

# The Roving Kind

How sad the tales of the innocent guy who got caught
by the gal with the gleam in her eye....

Words and music by Jessie Cavanaugh and Arnold Stanton

1. As I cruised out one e-ven-ing up-on a night's ca-reer,__ I
spied a lof-ty clip-per ship and to her I did steer. I
hist-ed out my sig-a-nals, which she so quick-ly knew,__ And

2. "Oh, par-don me," she says to me, "for be-ing out so late,__ For
if my par-ents heard of it then sad would be my fate. My
fa-ther is in pol-i-tics, a good and right-eous man,__ My

when she saw my bunt-ing fly, she im - me - diate-ly hove to.____
moth- er is an ac - ro - bat, I ___ do the best I can." ____

*(Chorus)*

She had a dark and a rov - ing ___ eye, _____ and her

hair hung down in ring - a - lets. ____ She was a nice girl, a

prop - er girl, but one of the rov - ing kind.

3. I took her for some fish and chips and treated her so fine,
   And hardly did I realize she was the roving kind.
   I kissed her lips, I missed her lips, and found to my surprise
   She was nothing but a pirate ship rigged up in a disguise. *(Chorus)*


4. So come all you good sailormen who sail the wintry sea,
   And come all you apprentice lads, a warning take from me:
   Beware of lofty clipper ships, they'll be the ruin of you.
   For 'twas there she made me walk the plank, and pushed me under too. *(Chorus)*

# My True Love (Martian Love Song)

In the days of space travel, will love still be unre-
quited?

*With tongue only slightly in cheek*

Words and music by XTRPL 8 (Lee Hays and Earl Robinson)

*(Chorus)*

My true love's an or-di-nar-y thing, You'd know her an-y — where —
By her pink an-ten-na and her pol-ka-dot skin And the
hy-dro-gen sul-fide of her hair.

1. Oh, my
2. We were

dar - ling, how I miss you, I nev-er need-ed you so much Till I
read - y to be mar-ried,— When an earth man led her a-stray, And I've

missed your crim-son eye-lids And the scales I love to touch. You're my
not seen my poor dar-ling Since that sad ga-lac-tic day. If you

cos - mic lit-tle sweet-heart And your thought waves are the most, Send-ing
meet her in Chi-ca-go Or on Ve-nus or Mer-cur-y And if

growls of love like thun-der Out a-long the Mar-tian coast.
you should hap-pen to rec-og-nize her, Send her back to

me (c. o. d.) Yes, my true love's an or - di - nar - y thing, You'd

know her an - y - where — By her pink an - ten - na and her

pol - ka - dot skin And the twen - ty - four dim - ples on her

chin- ny chin chin. (Well, they're not real - ly dim-ples, cause dim-ples turn in) And the

hy - dro - gen sul - fide of her hair.

# Kumbaya

It came to us as a song supposedly from Africa, and
it had only the one word. The pretty tune suggested
that it might be a lullaby, so we added a few lines to
make it that.

New words and new music arrangement by
Erik Darling, Ronnie Gilbert, Lee Hays and Fred Hellerman

# Sinner Man

It is an old song, but, as has happened with many spirituals and gospel songs, the group spent an evening improvising around the theme of the original and the result is not the old song, but the old song with sizable additions.

Additional words and arrangement by
Erik Darling, Ronnie Gilbert, Lee Hays and Fred Hellerman

Oh, sin-ner man, where you gon-na run to, All on that Day? Oh, sin-ner man, where you gon-na run to, Oh, sin-ner man, where you gon-na run to, Oh, sin-ner man,

moon-'ll be a-bleed-ing." Lord says, "Sin-ner man,— sea-'ll be a sink-ing."
should-'ve been a-pray-ing!" Lord says, "Sin-ner man,— should-'ve been a-pray-ing."

Lord says, "Sin-ner man, sun-'ll be a-freez-in' all on that Day!"
Lord says, "Sin-ner man! You should-'ve been a-pray-ing, all on that Day!"

all on that Day! _____

# I Never Will Marry

Fred Hellerman (who has often used the nom de plume Fred Brooks) rewrote the old song, but the opinions expressed in the new lyrics are not necessarily those of the author or the singers.

New words and new music by Fred Brooks (Fred Hellerman)

*Good-night waltz tempo*

Verse

say that love's a gen - tle thing, But it's on - ly
train pulled out, the whis - tle blew With a low and a

brought me pain, _____ 'Cause the on - ly man
lone - some moan; _____ He's gone, he's gone like the

ev - er loved Is gone on the mid - night train. I

morn - ing dew, And left me here a - lone.

*Chorus*

nev - er will mar - ry, I'll be no man's

wife, I ex - pect to live sin - gle

All the days of my life.

2. The      life. _____

3. There's many a change in the winter wind
   And a change in the cloud's design;
   There's many a change in a young man's heart,
   But never a change in mine. *(Chorus)*

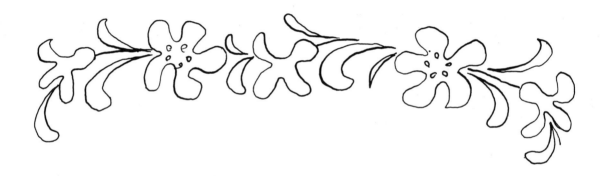

# The Sinking of the Reuben James

The *Reuben James* was sunk early in World War II, the first U.S. Naval victim of Hitler's submarines. Her crew list read like a roll call at the United Nations, so richly were America's national heritages represented. Woody Guthrie's original song was inspired by it. Fred Hellerman added the last stanza.

Words and music by Woody Guthrie. Last verse by Fred Hellerman

1. Have you heard of a ship called the good Reu - ben James, Manned by hard fight - ing men both of hon - or and of fame? She flew the Stars and Stripes of the

hun - dred men went down to their dark wa - ter - y grave; When that good ship went down, on - ly for - ty - four were saved. 'Twas the last day of Oc - to - ber that they

land _____ of the free,     But to - night she's in her _____
saved _____ for - ty - four     From the cold     ic - y

grave     at the bot-tom _ of the     sea. _____
wa - ters by the cold _____ Ice - land     shore. _____     Tell me,

*(Chorus)*

what were     their names,     tell me, what were     their names?     Did

you have     a friend     on the good Reu - ben James?     What were their

names, tell me, what were their names? Did you have a friend on the good Reu - ben James? _____ 2. One James? _____

3. It was there in the dark of that uncertain night
   That we watched for the U-boat and waited for a fight;
   Then a whine and a rock and a great explosion roared,
   And they laid the Reuben James on the cold ocean floor. *(Chorus)*

4. Well, many years have passed since those brave men are gone,
   And those cold icy waters are still and they're calm.
   Many years have passed, but still I wonder why
   The worst of men must fight and the best of men must die. *(Chorus)*

# Last Night I Had the Strangest Dream

Ed McCurdy wrote this moving vision of "that daz-
zling dream of ages."

*Moderately*

Words and music by Ed McCurdy

1. Last night I had the strang - est __ dream I'd __ nev - er
2. And when the pa - per was all __ signed, And a mil - lion

dreamed __ be - fore. _____ I dreamed the world had
cop - ies made, _____ They all joined hands and

all a - greed To put an end __ to war. _____ I
bowed their __ heads And grate - ful pray - ers were prayed. _____ And the

*FINE*

*D. C. al FINE*

dreamed I saw a might - y room And the room was
peo - ple in the streets be - low Were danc - ing

full of men; _____ And the pa - per they were
round and round, _____ While swords and guns and

sign - ing said They'd nev - er ___ fight a - gain. _____
u - ni - forms Were scat-tered ___ on the ground. _____

# Times A Gettin' Hard

Lee Hays wrote the words many years ago to tell the
story of a sharecropper family on the move in the
bleak thirties.

*Moderately*

New words and new music arrangement by Lee Hays

1. Times are get-tin' hard, boys, mon-ey's get-tin' scarce; If
2. Take my Bi-ble from the bed, shot-gun from the wall;

times don't get no bet-ter, boys, bound to leave this place.
Take old Sal and hitch her up, the wag-on for to haul.

Take my true love by the hand, lead her through the town;
Pile the chairs and beds up high, let noth-ing drag the ground;

Say good-by to ev'ry-one, good-by to ev'ry-one.
Sal can pull and we can push, we're bound to leave this town.

3. Made a crop a year ago, it withered to the ground;
   Tried to get some credit, but the banker turned me down.
   Goin' to Califor-ni-ay, where everything is green,
   Goin' to have the best old farm that you have ever seen.

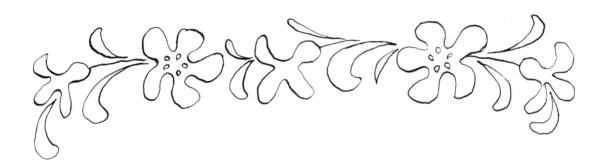

# On My Journey

Anyone who can resist singing, clapping the beat or stamping his feet when this one gets going probably has a worse cold than he thought and ought to be home in bed.

Melody traditional. New verses by
Erik Darling, Ronnie Gilbert, Lee Hays and Fred Hellerman

3. When the stars are fallin' and the thunder starts to roll,
   When the stars are fallin' and the thunder starts to roll,
   When the stars are fallin' and the thunder starts to roll,
   I don't want you to weep after me.

4. High up on the mountain, leave my sorrow down below,
   High up on the mountain, leave my sorrow down below,
   High up on the mountain, leave my sorrow down below,
   I don't want you to weep after me.

# Twelve Gates to the City

A gospel song with a particularly appealing vision of that place of peace wherein abide many tribes. This song seemed especially appropriate to The Weavers in a concert tour of Israel.

New words and new music arranged by
Erik Darling, Ronnie Gilbert, Lee Hays and Fred Hellerman

Three gates to the north, — and three in the south, — There's three in the east, —
— and three in the west. — There's twelve gates — to the
cit - y, — Hal - le - lu - - - jah. — Oh, oh, —

**Chorus**

Oh, what a beau-ti-ful cit-y, Oh, what a beau-ti-ful cit-y,

Oh, what a beau-ti-ful cit-y, Twelve gates___ to the cit-y,___ Hal-le-lu-

*FINE*

- - - jah.___

*Verse*

1. Well, there are so man-y ways___ to
2. And you can walk right___ in___ and you'll be

get to the cit-y,
wel-come in the cit-y,

So man-y ways___ to get to the cit-y, There are
Walk right___ in___and you'll be wel-come in the cit-y, You can

175

so man-y ways____ to get to the cit-y,___ Twelve gates____ to the
walk right in and you'll be wel-come in the cit-y, ___ Twelve gates____ to the

cit-y, ___ Hal - le -lu - - jah.___ Oh, oh, _____
cit-y, ___ Hal - le -lu - - jah.___ Oh, oh, _____

3. And you can come from the east to the middle of the city,
You can come from the west to the middle of the city,
And we will meet all together in the middle of the city,
Twelve gates to the city, Hallelu-u-jah. *(Chorus)*

# Index